The Scientific Approach

The
Scientific
Approach

J. T. DAVIES

*Professor and Head of the Department
of Chemical Engineering, University of
Birmingham, England*

ACADEMIC PRESS . 1965
LONDON and NEW YORK

ACADEMIC PRESS INC. (LONDON) LTD
Berkeley Square House
Berkeley Square
London, W.1.

U.S. Edition published by

ACADEMIC PRESS INC.
111 Fifth Avenue
New York, New York 10003

MADE AND PRINTED IN GREAT BRITAIN BY
WILLIAM CLOWES AND SONS, LIMITED, LONDON AND BECCLES

Preface

Although the concept of the "two cultures" is unfortunately often valid in administrative practice, the basic creative approaches in arts and in science are very similar. The enquiring mind respects none of the boundaries between different disciplines: a new unification may have a poetic beauty irrespective of whether one achieves it in words, in paint or in scientific concepts.

Indeed, through the rash hopes, the occasional moments of furious excitement, and the frequent bitter disappointments in creative science, one comes to experience a philosophical approach which is common to the creation of *any* idea which is a little different from that which has been expressed before.

Having studied at times mathematics, physical chemistry and chemical engineering, and having had also the privilege, as a student in 1944–45, of being guided in the philosophy of science by Professor Sir Karl Popper, I have been able to examine at first hand, during my career in research, various basic principles and unifying concepts in the philosophy of science.

It is to record these ideas and also to illustrate scientific method (without presenting a vast collection of factual results), that I have written this little book. There are particular references to the *changes* in the approach to science from classical times through the Renaissance to the present, wherein the reader may find bridges between C. P. Snow's "two cultures". The book is written in terms comprehensible to students both of the humanities and of science and engineering.

June, 1965   J. T. Davies

Acknowledgements

It is a pleasure to express my gratitude to:

Professor Sir Karl Popper, whose inimitably enthusiastic teaching in 1944–45 first aroused my interest in the philosophy of science. Our subsequent meetings have invariably strengthened this interest; and his many philosophical publications over the last 32 years have always been a source of inspiration.

Dr. H. V. Stopes-Roe, of the University of Birmingham, for many stimulating discussions, particularly on the subjects of Chapters 2, 3 and 4. But for his friendly criticism, this book would have contained many incomplete ideas and errors.

Professor A. A. Walters, of the University of Birmingham, for discussions on economic theory, and for his making available to me certain of his provisional conclusions.

Professor R. Pascal, of the University of Birmingham, for reading the proofs and making constructive suggestions for improvement.

My wife Ruth, who has debunked much masculine nonsense with a happy blend of reasoning, common sense and feminine intuition.

CONTENTS

Preface v
Acknowledgements vii

Chapter 1   THE ORIGIN OF THEORIES

Introduction 1
The "Truth" of Theories 4
The Origin of Theories 11

Chapter 2   THE TESTING OF THEORIES

Introduction 18
Are Experiments Superfluous? 20
Some Examples of Experimenting 22
The Motivation for Experimenting 29
Summary 31

Chapter 3   CONFIRMATION AND CONFIDENCE

When is a Theory "Scientific"? 32
Discrepancies between Theoretical Predictions and Observa-
 tional Results 38
Attributes of a Scientific Theory 40
Summary 42

Chapter 4   ENGINEERING AND SCIENCE

Theories and the Engineer 43
Strategy in Engineering 44
Design in Engineering 48
Strategy in Science 49
Confidence and Credibility 50
Summary 52

Chapter 5   THE SIMPLE LAWS OF SCIENCE

Introduction 53
Simplicity 54

Examples of Simple Laws 55
Conventions and Simple Laws 58
The Abundance of Simple Laws 60

Chapter 6 PREDICTION AND PROBABILITY

Predictions 68
The Role of Theory in Prediction 71
Probability Theory 80

Chapter 7 SCIENCE AND SOCIETY

Science and Our Civilization 82
Operational Research 86
Historical Theories 89
Economic Theories 93

References 97
Index 99

Chapter 1

The Origin of Theories

There is no logical path to these laws; only intuition, resting on a sympathetic understanding of experience, can reach them. (1918)

As far as the laws of mathematics refer to reality, they are not certain; and as far as they are certain, they do not refer to reality. (1921)

Concepts, considered logically, never originate in experience; i.e. they are not to be derived from experience alone. (1930)

It is only by speculation that it [the external world] can become comprehensible to us. From this it follows that our conceptions of physical reality can never be definitive; we must always be ready to alter them; to alter, that is, the axiomatic basis of physics, in order to take account of the facts of perception with the greatest possible logical completeness. (1931)

ALBERT EINSTEIN

INTRODUCTION

Certitude and complete objectivity are commonly and erroneously believed to be the criteria of science. Perhaps to these misapprehensions should be added yet another, the idea that science consists of a painstaking series of labours undertaken to gather a collection of random facts, from which one then deduces a general theory which is always true. It is to correct these impressions and to help bridge the gap between the "two cultures" that this book on scientific method has been written. It is much more important, both for the man who pursues the arts and for the scientist, to appreciate the *methods* of science than merely to learn a large number of results of scientific experiments. Science is no omnipotent goddess; it is the scientific attitude, as manifest in theory and experiment, in which we believe.

Let us first consider the procedure by which a particular experiment is selected as being worthwhile. Science, as Sir Karl Popper (1945, 1962) has pointed out, is much more than a mere "body of facts"; it is a *collection* of data from experiments and observations, the collection having been assembled according to the collectors' interests and points

1

of view. These are determined by preconceived ideas, which when crystallized in the mind in potentially experimental terms, are called scientific theories. With some theory in mind, we *select* from the infinite variety of possible experiments and observations those that are relevant to this theory. But we do not select *only* such facts as are in accord with the theory; we (or our scientific rivals) are prepared to find experimental results which may show a flaw in the theory, so that it must then be modified, or abandoned in favour of a better theory.

Popper (1945, 1962) has suggested a most apt analogy, likening a theory to a searchlight, in the beam of which certain things are made visible, though their appearance must depend on the position of the searchlight, upon its intensity, its colour and the way it is directed. But the objects illuminated are also contributing to whether or not they become visible, and to how they appear at any given time; and, similarly, a scientific description will depend upon our selection and upon our point of view, these stemming from our preconceived theory about how we expect the system to behave. Scientific description is, however, not *entirely* subjective; it depends on, and is limited by, the external system being studied. This "searchlight" analogy can be

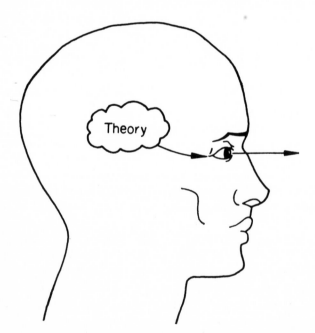

Fig. 1.1. Significant aspect of Popper's "searchlight" analogy of the human select and study facts in the light of our theoretical interests.

applied equally well to creative studies generally, including the fine arts, and historical writing. The common feature is that we *select* material which appeals aesthetically and which excites our curiosity.

This approach is in contrast to that of the empiricists down to and including Hume, who held that knowledge streams into us through our senses, and that to avoid distorting such knowledge, and thereby introducing error, we should remain entirely passive and receptive. Popper has called this the "bucket" theory of the mind. A modern version of it appears in B. Blackstone's biography of Virginia Woolf: "Surrounding the human synthesis we have this great mystery of nature. Perhaps it is chaos, perhaps it will reveal a pattern. We don't

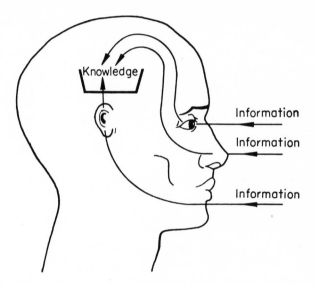

Fig. 1.2. Significant aspect of "bucket" analogy of the mind. According to this, we should avoid distorting knowledge coming into our minds through our senses, by being as receptive and as passive as possible.

know. And the danger is this: that pattern making, 'one-making'," as she called it in her last novel, "Between the Acts", "is so inveterate a habit of the human mind that it makes clear vision very difficult. We want to see a pattern, and a pattern obediently appears."

Note here the words "danger" and "clear vision"; they contrast strongly with the "searchlight" view, which is preferred by V. S. Pritchett: "If we look at modern autobiographies of all sorts, we see that they are best when they are fragmentary: unabashed introspections like Mr. Cyril Connolly's account of Eton, or sweeping statements like George Orwell's. Or, when they reject ordinary chronology, and are autobiographies ruled by a subject: T. E. Lawrence's 'Seven Pillars'. Modern autobiography fails when it has no attitude, when it has no special subject which rescues the self from the cliché of having lived. There is no credit in living; the credit is in being able to specify experience."

Which of these philosophical theories is to be preferred, the "searchlight" theory or the "bucket" theory? How can we choose between them? The answer to these questions lies partly in our personal feelings, our awareness of being passive or active. Are we *conscious* of selecting data to test a preconceived idea? Is there, in other words, a psychological flaw in either theory? Further, to help decide between these philosophical theories we should also ask ourselves which of them has the greater share of the virtues of lucidity, simplicity, neatness and generality. We may ask also whether either has a logical flaw, and here the difficulty of explaining how we could rigorously induce a *general* theory from observations of particular events is indeed a difficulty of the "bucket" theory. Throughout this book the "searchlight" theory will be followed; the reader will be able to judge, both from his own awareness and from the quoted accounts of experimental studies, which theory he prefers.

THE "TRUTH" OF THEORIES

Let us now consider, as an example, the extremely simple theory that "all cats have tails". We call this a theory, but we might equally well call it an idea, a generalization, an hypothesis, a notion, a supposition or even a correlation between cats and tails; the word used makes no logical difference. In our example, some slight curiosity and interest in cats has led us to propose this theory that all cats have tails, and we now look around with enhanced interest (as if with a searchlight) to see whether the theory "works", i.e. we are now trying to extend the theory as widely as possible, testing it by observation. Of course, in the present example, someone will soon show us, assuming that we have not observed it first, that there *are* cats without tails; the theory does *not* always work, and so we now withdraw it and hope for the inspiration to put forward a better theory. Our original theory, simple as it was, was not quite useless; it led us, and perhaps others, to examine cats more carefully. This, in general, is the great value of theories: not only do they help to unify the subject matter, but they play a leading role predicting events and so stimulating experiments and observations; they are as important in science as is inspiration in poetry and painting, or love in human encounters. Without these activities of the mind, and the emotional drive to achieve them, human life would have been drab indeed, and science would have been no more an intellectual adventure than collecting pebbles on the beach.

Can a theory ever be "true"? We can see the answer to this if we assume that in looking at cats we have seen a hundred with tails and none without. But clearly this will not make the theory true. Indeed, one never talks of general scientific theories as "true"; they are at best *not disproved*, as if a cynical judge never pronounced the accused innocent, but only "not guilty yet"! To avoid confusion, the word "true" should be reserved for propositions in logic and in pure mathematics. By way of a concession, however, scientists dignify certain careful and successful tests of a theory as "confirmations" of that theory, but these can be neither proofs nor "verifications" of theory. Another concession lies in referring to simple, well-tested theories having a wide range of applicability as "laws" of science, but these laws, just like other theories, have no logical status and may conceivably be disproved at any time. The disproof within the last decade of the "law of parity" in atomic physics is an example of this.

It will have been noticed that the scientific cat-spotter is looking at cats for a particular reason—to check his theory. He may not be a cat-lover, but even if he is, he may not have time to indulge his emotions. This is generally true in science: the scientist's way of thought emphasizes general concepts at the expense of a sensation of individuality of each separate event or object; the more general the theoretical concepts the further removed they are from sensual apprehension. The processes of generalization and of symbolization represent in every field of endeavour the highest intellectual activity of which man is capable, whether it be belief in a God, the painting of a masterpiece, the writing of tragedy or the building of a vast and unifying scheme of scientific interpretation. As Poincaré wrote, referring to the intellectual elegance of many scientific theories, "Le savant n'étudie pas la nature parce que cela est utile; il l'étudie parce qu'il y prend plaisir, et il y prend plaisir parce qu'elle est belle. Si la nature n'était pas belle, elle ne vaudrait pas la peine d'être connue, la vie ne vaudrait pas la peine d'être vécue."

It is convenient here to digress a little on the difference between observation and experiment. The former implies that we are merely studying, the latter that we are making an effort to control or alter the system in a particular way for the purpose of study. Thus we have been merely *observing* cats with tails in the above example, whereas with a little unkind *experimentation* we could at once have disproved the theory and so saved ourselves further tedious observation. This greater power and intellectual neatness of the experimental approach over the observational method is fairly general, and a great deal of ingenuity is put into devising the neatest experimental approach to a problem, just as one wishes in a game of chess to win by an elegant demonstration of power and economy of moves rather than by a long-drawn-out slogging match. Into forming a theory goes the imagination of the scientist, into the planning of his experiments goes his art, and into the actual measurements go his crafts.

If experiments cannot be made, as has, for example, been true of astronomy and space studies in the past, one must rely on making the most appropriate observations. In a way we are all theoretical astronomers. Most of us hold among our theories that (apart from fog or cloud cover) the sun will rise over England again every morning. Although this theory, like the "all cats have tails" theory and all other theories or generalizations, has no logical status whatever, still if we are betting men we doubtless have a preference as to which of these predictions we should place our money on. We should bet on the "sunrise" prediction as being in accord with observation rather than on the "all cats have tails" idea. Bertrand Russell coined a useful term when he referred to the "degree of credibility" of a proposition. It is not a question of mathematical probabilities; rather it is much more like predicting the results of elections or horse races, where we are well aware that we do not have all the knowledge we need, and where different bookmakers will accept different odds. We can never, of course, know all the factors that may come into operation; all we can do is to study as many relevant factors as possible and then assume that others will not become operative. As with horses, some theories of a phenomenon are favourites and some are outsiders; as with the horses only a practical test will show us which hypothesis works best. But placing bets or asserting our confidence before the race or the experiment is a far cry, both logically and in practice, from asserting a precise mathematical probability based on past form.

A simple example which illustrates this is the experiment of tossing a penny. Suppose that on starting this experiment we find that heads have appeared four times consecutively; will this alter our bets that tails will come up the fifth time? Most of us would ignore the immediate past form and say the chance was still 0·5; others, more cynical, might believe that the coin was loaded. Hence we have the necessity for further experiment. The same uncertainty, stemming from possible ignorance of some additional factor, makes the application of mathematical probability theory logically indefensible in scientific predictions.

Indeed, mathematical probability, like other mathematical deductions, is part of a strictly logical system, and is always "true" in the sense that, given the premises and the deductive rules to be used, the result has been obtained correctly. Truth is thus a word we may use of a mathematical or logical deduction, but it is not one we should ever use of a scientific theory. The latter can at best be described as a well-tested and precise working hypothesis.

Many scientific theories, particularly in the physical sciences, are, of course, highly mathematical in form, and one may well ask at this point just what is the relation between mathematics and physics. A few simple examples are appropriate here. In pure mathematics, one

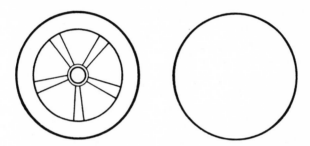

FIG. 1.3. Comparison of wheel and perfect circle.

defines a perfect circle, and then shows that its circumference s is equal to π times its diameter d, i.e.

$$s = \pi d. \tag{i}$$

One can now apply this idea to a wheel, the physical theory being that the wheel is a perfect circle. The mathematical formulation of this theory would then give

$$\text{circumference of wheel} = \pi \times \text{diameter of wheel}. \tag{ii}$$

It is clear that this is not quite the same as eq. (i): we have *identified* the circumference of the wheel with s, and the diameter of the wheel with d, so that while eq. (i) is necessarily correct, eq. (ii) is only as correct as our identification of the wheel with the circle. This identification may or may not be reasonable, depending on the wheel; at best it will be accurate to several significant figures. There is no logical reason for the identification, its only justification is that it may work well in practice. Even if a theory works well today, it may not do so tomorrow, for a wheel may have unsuspected internal stresses, and deform itself before our next measurement.

Galileo in 1623 stated very explicitly his belief in the importance of quantitative theories containing mathematical symbols which were to be identified with observational quantities. He wrote that "nature is written in mathematical language". His theories of the motion of bodies are good examples of this quantitative approach. In 1638 he realized that every body remains in a state of rest or of uniform motion unless an impressed force (f) compels it to change that state. He also understood the concept of acceleration—that the velocity of fall (v) of a body is directly proportional to the time (t) for which it has fallen.

When Galileo formulated these two theories, he did so with a wide background of experience of the study of falling bodies. Indeed, in 1632, discussing the behaviour of bodies falling towards the earth, he had written, "Everyone knows that this cause is called gravity.... We know no more about the virtue causing a stone to drop than we do about the virtue tending to keep a projectile aloft, or about the virtue which guides the moon in its orbit."

This was the historical setting in which, several decades later, Newton (1642–1727) made his great theoretical contributions to the science of mechanics. His first "law" is essentially the one put forward by Galileo, that bodies remain in a state of rest or of uniform motion unless an impressed force changes this state. His second "law" is a mathematical theory stating explicitly that the *change of motion* of a body is directly proportional to the impressed force (f) ; or, in modern terminology, $\mathrm{d}(mv)\mathrm{d}t = f$ or $m(\mathrm{d}v/\mathrm{d}t) = f$, where m is to be identified with the mass of the body, v with its velocity and t with time. The product mv represents momentum, and $(\mathrm{d}v/\mathrm{d}t)$ represents acceleration.

Newton went on to propound his famous quantitative theory relating gravity (considered as a force) to the mutual attraction of masses and to acceleration. Voltaire was given to understand from Newton's niece that this theory of gravitation originated when Newton saw an apple fall from a tree as he was sitting one day in his orchard. This, to use Einstein's phrase, was part of the experience, of which a sympathetic understanding led him intuitively to produce his mathematical theory of gravity.

This theory (in modern terminology) states that the force between two bodies of masses m_1 and m_2 is given by $f = Gm_1m_2/r^2$, where G is a constant and r is to be identified with the distance between the centres of the bodies. Combination with the second "law" then gives the theoretical prediction that the acceleration of any body towards a mass m_1 should be Gm_1/r^2.

Newton applied his theory to the movement of the moon. He wrote that in 1666 he "began to think of gravity extending to the orb of the moon... and thereby compared the force requisite to keep the moon in her orb with the force of gravity at the surface of the Earth, and found them to answer pretty well." This successful and elegant testing of theoretical predictions against observation is discussed further in Chapter 2.

Later, Newton went on to apply his theories to planetary motion; and, by thus identifying the symbols of his quantitative theory with celestial masses and distances, he predicted that the acceleration of any planet towards the sun should vary inversely as the square of the distance from the sun, with the corollary that the paths of the planets should be ellipses.

Another common identification is that of the force f around an electrical charge decreasing with distance r from the charge in the inverse way to which the area of a sphere increases with its radius. On this theory, our identification gives:

$$f = 1/r^2 \tag{iii}$$

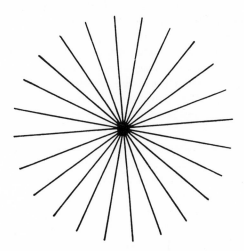

FIG. 1.4. Lines of force are spherically symmetrical around an isolated point charge or mass.

where the quantities refer to the electrical system. If eq. (iii) were a *purely mathematical* equation applied to an ideal sphere it would necessarily always be true, but when f and r refer to the electrical charge field, all we can say is that it may or may not be an accurate representation of what we have found in our experiment. As mentioned above, a similar equation describes, with the same limitations, the gravitational field around a body, and, as with the electrical field, the equation (iii) has worked well in practice, surviving frequent precise tests.

A rather illuminating example of identification comes from a mathematical theory of the universe expounded by Professor E. Schrödinger. He considers a mathematical 4-dimensional hyper-surface, which, to be made visualizable, is reduced to an ordinary (i.e. defined by x, y, z) one-shell equilateral hyperboloid, (H). Now the first important identification is made: his theory is that "we shall now interpret z as world time. This is, of course, not necessary; later on we shall contemplate other choices...with z taken as time, the parallel circles on (H) represent space at different times. Thus the circumference of space... contracts up to a certain epoch, $z = 0$, and then expands." With such theoretical identifications the geometrical model is taken to represent a physical theory of space, time and events. This is successful, both in that it unifies mathematically the concepts of space and time, and also in that the mathematical equations can be solved quite simply. Is it therefore a completely satisfactory *scientific* theory?

To answer this question we must consider the criteria of successful scientific theories. These, as we have seen, differ from pure mathematics and logic, in which fields we can prove that a deduction must be true; in science, experimental tests are necessary. It is important, therefore, when one reads a book like Professor Schrödinger's, to distinguish what is pure mathematics and what is the physical theory. As Jeans said of Eddington's theory of the numerical basis of physics and of the universe, it is hard to know why the theory should not apply equally well to an orange.

It is this procedure of identification that makes mathematical physics different from mathematics. Pure mathematics itself is necessarily correct if it is self-consistent and if the deductions are logical, but the identifications of a theory are subject to no rules except that they should work and be simple. Schrödinger identifies his symbol z with time, his τ-derivatives with field functions, A^2 with rest density, and $A^2\phi_4$ with weight, stating for example that "$A^2\phi_4$ fulfils the requirements of a reasonable weight function, since its space integral is a constant".

Two criteria (amongst others, see pp. 33, 40) must be satisfied by any satisfactory theory: it must unify and show the relation between previously unconnected quantities (such as space and time), and it must be simple enough for *critical* experimental checks to be formulated. Only thus can identifications be justified. The observational tests of Schrödinger's theory are not very clear-cut, but he found nothing to invalidate his theory.

THE ORIGIN OF THEORIES

In producing a general theory, the human brain cannot be represented as a comparing machine. Having evolved a theory, however, one then identifies the symbols in the theory with the results of practical studies, and finally deduces (and this step may well be comparison) testable consequences from these generalizations. What *is* the origin of a scientific theory? This is a question that has caused much speculation and argument. There seems to be no simple answer; one can only say

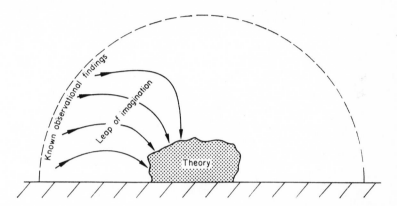

FIG. 1.5. A theory arises by inspiration, i.e. by an illogical leap of the imagination. One needs, of course, a factual background; the creation of a theory requires what Einstein called a "sympathetic understanding of experience".

that a theory arises from a leap of the imagination, from inspiration, or from "the creative approach". Theories are generalizations and unifications, and as such they cannot logically follow only from our experiences of a few particular events. Indeed we often generalize from a single event, just as a dog does who, having once seen a cat in a certain driveway, looks eagerly around whenever he passes that place in future. Evidently this latter activity is equivalent to testing the theory (admittedly of low excellence, see p. 41) that "there is always a cat in that driveway".

But even scientific theories of greater excellence, which unify intellectual concepts, can never be wholly abstract; at their best, such theories cover a wide range of experiments and observations, the influence of which cannot be ignored in the formulation of a theory. They furnish what Einstein called a "sympathetic understanding of experience" against the background of which, by an intuitive leap of imagination, a generalization may be evolved. And, as has often been said, research can be planned but discovery cannot.

Bearing in mind that theories thus evolved cannot have any logical status, i.e. that they are *all* merely working hypotheses, we can more readily accept the roles which analogies and even dreams can play in giving rise to scientific theories. Examples which come to mind are the analogy between the wheel and the perfect circle and the analogy between molecules and little hard spheres. Another example of the fertile process of imaginative analogy, of transplanting an idea from one field of endeavour to another, is illustrated by Charles Darwin's account of the inception of his theory of the formation of coral islands. His theory of 1842 was that the coral organisms built up the reefs from

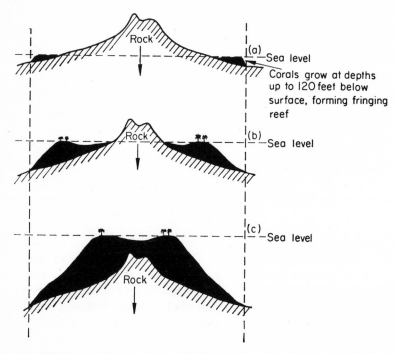

Fig. 1.6. Diagrams to show how, by subsidence of a rocky island, a fringing reef (a) round a rocky island gives rise to a barrier reef (b). Further slow subsidence of the island results in an atoll ring, shown in (c), underlying which there is predicted to be, on this theory, a thick cap of limestone formed from the skeletons of dead corals. This figure is adapted from Darwin's original diagrams.

mountains which had once had their peaks above the surface of the ocean, but which had gradually subsided. In this way could be explained elegantly the ring-shape of the barrier-reef of coral encircling an island

FIG. 1.7. Coral island off Viti Levu, Fiji. The stage of evolution is that of Fig. 1–6b. (Photograph by Aerofilms and Aero Pictorial, Ltd.)

and of the fringing-reef lying near the shore of a typical coral island. He wrote, "No other work of mine was begun in so deductive a spirit as this, for the whole theory was thought out on the west coast of South America, before I had seen a true coral reef. I had therefore only to verify and extend my views by a careful examination of living reefs. But it should be observed that I had during the two previous years

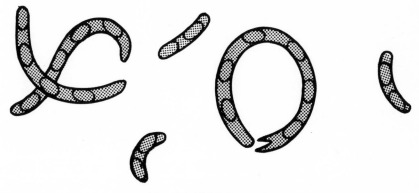

FIG. 1.8. Kekúlé's dream.

been incessantly attending to the effects on the shores of South America of the intermittent elevation of the land, together with denudation and the deposition of sediment. This necessarily led me to reflect much on the effects of subsidence, and it was easy to replace in imagination the continued deposition of sediment by the upward growth of corals. To do this was to form my theory of the formation of barrier-reefs and atolls." The theory was simple, elegant and attractive; the tests undertaken in recent years to test Darwin's theory that subsidence had occurred are described in the next chapter.

The classical example of a dream leading to a scientific theory is that which led to Kekulé's theory of 1865: that in aromatic organic chemistry six carbon atoms are linked into a ring that persists intact through many chemical reactions which change certain atoms attached to this

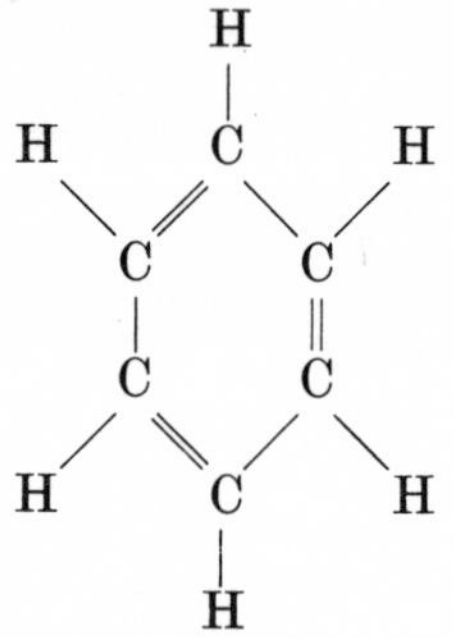

FIG. 1.9. Structural formula of benzene, from chemical theory.

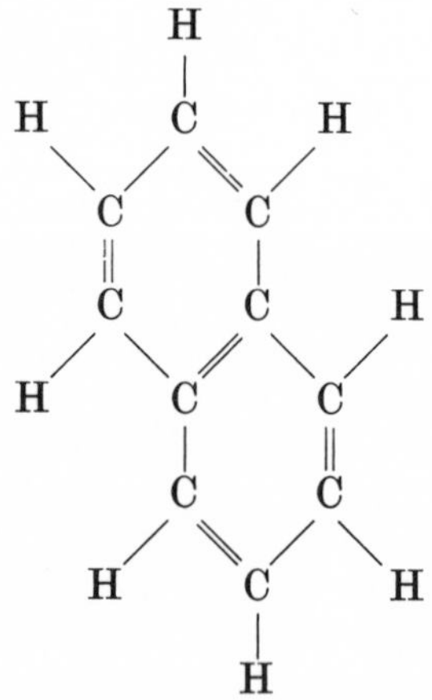

FIG. 1.10. Structural formula of naphthalene (two benzene rings condensed together), according to chemical theory.

ring. Kekulé's theory is as famous for its origin as for its success. "I was sitting", he reported, "writing at my textbook; but the work did not progress; my thoughts were elsewhere.

"I turned my chair to the fire and dozed. Again the atoms were gambolling before my eyes. This time the smaller groups kept modestly in the background. My mental eye, rendered more acute by repeated visions of the kind, could now distinguish larger structures, of manifold conformation: long rows, sometimes more closely fitted together; all twining and twisting in snake-like motion. But look! What was that?

FIG. 1.11. Model of naphthalene molecule, built from scale models of atoms. This is based upon both chemical theory and the X-ray scattering from various atoms and simple molecules.

One of the snakes had seized hold of its own tail, and the form whirled mockingly before my eyes. As if by a flash of lightning I awoke; and this time also I spent the rest of the night in working out the consequences of the hypothesis.

"Let us learn to dream, gentlemen", said Kekulé, "and then perhaps we shall learn the truth." But, he added, "let us beware of publishing our dreams before they have been put to the proof by the waking understanding."

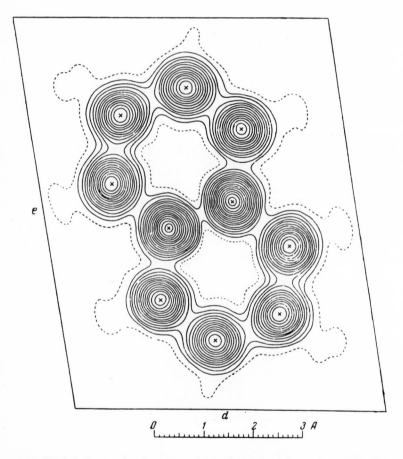

FIG. 1.12. Naphthalene molecule as completely determined from the purely physical method of X-ray analysis. This is a map of electron density in the molecular plane, lines corresponding to increments of 0·5 electrons per 10^{-24} cm³. The outermost (corresponding to a density of 0·5 electron per 10^{-24} cm³) shows obvious projections due to hydrogen atoms. This picture, in which the magnification is 130,000,000 times, was published by Abrahams, Robertson and White, in *Acta Cryst.* **2**, 238 (1949).

Kekulé's dream, illogical and non-quantitative as it was, provided a simple and unifying key to aromatic organic chemistry. His theory played a leading role in stimulating experiment; modern investigations involving electron diffraction and X-ray studies (Figure 1.12) have confirmed Kekulé's simple analogy, and it has proved valuable over a wide range of phenomena.

Summarizing, we see that scientific method involves curiosity and interest in the world about us, leading to the formulation by some obscure process of the mind of a generalization or "theory" about it. We could equally well have called our theory a supposition, a correlation or an hypothesis; whether it is mathematical in form or not is beside the point. We, and other people too, will wish to see how widely our theory is true, and so we (and they) check its predictions by observation or experiment, over as wide a range as we can, to see whether it will or will not hold. We can never prove a theory to be generally true, because at any time some new experimental observation may invalidate it. A theory has no logical status, nor can mathematical probability be applied to its powers of prediction; its importance lies in its predictions leading us on to further investigations.

Chapter 2
The Testing of Theories

INTRODUCTION

Theories were numerous in the ancient world, but concerning experimental tests there was generally little opportunity and even less interest. Nearly two thousand years elapsed before an unprecedented confluence of cultural, religious and technological changes produced an environment in which *testing* theories by experiment and observation became normal practice, so that theories which were too vague or too complicated to be tested were no longer given serious consideration.

This modern outlook had its origins in the Renaissance which swept Italy in the fifteenth century, and which gradually made itself felt north of the Alps. Included in the Renaissance was a renewed interest in the numerical mathematical traditions of Pythagoras and Plato, and it was the threefold coincidence of this interest in mathematics, of the improving optical, time-keeping and metallurgical techniques, and of the Reformation (in the early decades of the sixteenth century), that led to the intellectual climate so extraordinarily favourable to the scientific ideas and experiments which erupted into activity at the beginning of the seventeenth century. In addition to these three factors, and possibly one reason for the vigour of the Reformation, was the rather unstable structure of European society at that time. It was an age of the decay of feudalism, of the generation of a new, vigorous and self-reliant mercantile and sea-faring society. And in these circumstances intelligence and the increasing literacy had a greater scope than hitherto.

Copernicus (1473–1543) is sometimes regarded as one of the first scientists in the modern sense. From his heliocentric theory of what is now called the solar system, he predicted the movements of heavenly bodies, and tried to test these predictions using the rather inadequate instruments available at that time. He found that his own predictions were confirmed, while those from Ptolemy's epicyclic theory were not : by his experiments he thus provided examples of confirmation and refutation.

Scientific progress was, however, generally very slight during the middle of the sixteenth century, and it was only through further spread of anti-dogmatic religious movements, with their emphases on the repudiation of authority and the freedom of individuals to indulge in critical discussions of each other's ideas, that experimental science could flourish.

By the beginning of the seventeenth century, this more critical attitude, coupled with an advancing technology, had rendered possible more accurate instruments such as clocks, telescopes, thermometers and compound microscopes; consequently, testing of scientific theories could be more exact and extensive than at any former time in history. Such was the origin of the flowering of scientific activity which occurred in the seventeenth century: technology and the new theories were (and are still) advancing hand in hand, each strengthening the other. Galileo began his experiments on the period of oscillation of pendulums in 1581, and his experiments on timing falling bodies were undertaken in 1589–91. In 1610 there appeared an account of his observations with his telescope, including his discovery of the satellites of the planet Jupiter, which confirmed the heliocentric theory of Copernicus.

But, for his views, particularly his development of the Copernican theory of the solar system, Galileo was condemned by the Inquisition, privately in 1616 and then publicly in 1633, on which occasion he recanted and promised never again to maintain that the Earth rotates or revolves.* Bertrand Russell maintains that in this way the Inquisition was successful in putting an end to science in Italy, where it did not revive for centuries.

In England in 1600, William Gilbert published his famous book " De Magnete ", in which he emphasized the importance of *new* phenomena, and of investigation by experiment. He related the magnetism of the earth, for example, to its rotation on its axis.

During the early decades of the seventeenth century, the English philosopher Francis Bacon wrote of the importance of experiment and observation, since knowledge, he maintained, was *useful* in giving man sovereignty over nature. He advocated a keen exchange of intellectual views, and thought that destructive criticism was particularly important. He further emphasized the importance of generalizations and of a fundamental approach, in that theories being tested should also be applied in new circumstances. For such testing, he stated,

---

*Note added in proof. In June 1965, almost three and a half centuries later, Pope Paul VI formally praised Galileo, together with Dante and Michelangelo, as "great spirits" of "immortal memory".

certain observations are found to be especially valuable in that they allow one to decide between two rival theories: respect for nature is the precondition of mastery.

Theories were gradually becoming public rather than private—they were more widely disseminated by the relatively newly invented (1440) printing press. Theories were also often useful, particularly in their applications to navigation, and in the waging of wars. Theories which were accurate and which stood up to repeated testing were clearly the best theories.

The modern scientific approach was now established, and theories which correlated the new measurements and predicted new findings were so highly regarded that some (such as Newton's theory in 1687 of the elliptical paths of the planets under an inverse square attractive force) were often considered to give a glimpse of absolute truth. This attitude was by no means always held, but when it was, it was sometimes maintained emphatically. In recent times it has been held that experimental chemistry is unnecessary; that it is a thing of the past. The mathematical theories of quantum mechanics of molecular orbitals could, with sufficient development, predict precisely the results which would be found in any given chemical experiment. A similar view was put forward by the late Sir Arthur Eddington (1933, 1939) in relation to physics. Since the theories of mathematical physics often predict experimental results correctly, he argued, the experiments are superfluous: the true theory will give us *a priori* knowledge.

ARE EXPERIMENTS SUPERFLUOUS?

If one can have *a priori* knowledge of observational results, not only does the theory make any experiment unnecessary, but further, if the experiment *is* carried out, and if the results disagree with theory, the theoretical value may be more accurate than the experiment. For example, Eddington believed that his theoretical value of 137·000 for the "fine structure constant" of physics was more accurate than the experimental figure of $137·0302 \pm 0·016$.

Where then, if we follow this argument, does the *a priori* knowledge come from? Eddington maintained that certain theoretical relations necessarily followed from the ways we looked at objects and measured them, illustrating his argument with an analogy of catching fish in a net. His illustration runs as follows. Suppose that, to investigate the natural history of fishes, a man casts a net into the water and brings up a fishy assortment. He then examines his catch for information on the size distribution of fish. He theorizes from his observations, according to

FIG. 2.1. Smaller fish pass through mesh, but larger ones are caught.

Eddington, that there is no fish of size less than two inches; a piece of knowledge that one should have been able to infer merely from a study of the method of approach to the problem (i.e. from the mesh size of the net), without the necessity of carrying out the experiment (see Fig. 2.1).

There are, however, serious objections to this analogy. In the first place the fisherman should *not* have deduced that "there are no fish of size less than two inches"; what he *might* more justifiably have deduced was that his net would not catch fish less than two inches in size. But even the latter conclusion is open to objections on the grounds that occasionally several fishes each smaller than two inches will become wedged in one mesh, and so caught. Further, one needs and assumes a

FIG. 2.2. Several small fish may block the net, and so become caught.

great deal of information about the system: for example, how each fish lies across a mesh; whether in practice the meshes have shrunk or stretched or have otherwise been deformed in the water, and so on. So the fishing-net argument, which Eddington used to justify the existence of *a priori* knowledge, is as full of holes as the net itself. Even apart from these objections to *a priori* knowledge, there is the illogicality of the necessary step of identifying the mathematical symbols with the results of the experiments. Experiments really *are* necessary.

SOME EXAMPLES OF EXPERIMENTING

Through the ages it had been commonly believed that heavier bodies always fell faster than lighter ones. While there were indeed grounds for believing this as it applies to a cannon ball relative to a leaf or a feather, it was believed to be true for all objects. It could, of course, have easily been tested at any time by (for example) dropping rocks of different weights over a cliff, but the experiment was not made till Galileo, in his famous series of experiments of 1589–91, dropped various heavy bodies of different weights from the Leaning Tower of Pisa : they all reached the ground at the same time, thereby effectively refuting the earlier theory handed down from the ancients to the professors and students then at Pisa University.

It was, of course, the prevailing attitudes that had prevented the test being carried out earlier. Even in 1591 Galileo became so unpopular for his experiments that he resigned his position at Pisa forthwith, and withdrew to Florence. His experiments, however, together with his ideas on dynamics (particularly on the concept of acceleration), and his demonstration that the path of a projectile was close to a parabola, were evidence of a new consciousness both of the concept of "time" and of the necessity for experimental tests. Scientific method was becoming established by practising scientists if not by professional philosophers.

Newton's theory of gravitational forces was, from its inception, extensively tested against observation and experiment. We have seen (p. 8) how in 1666 he calculated from his theory the magnitudes of the force of gravity at different distances from the earth, and compared his results with the forces required to keep the moon in her orbit. He "found them to answer pretty well". His later theoretical prediction that the planets should move in elliptical paths, under the action of the force of gravity, was also consistent with observation. His theories also predicted the precession of the equinoxes, and the variation of gravitational force with latitude. From the observed variations in the moon's motion it was predicted that the earth must be flattened in the ratio 1/230, compared with the modern figure of 1/297. Tidal theory was placed on a firm foundation, and the trajectory of comets and their periodic appearances could be predicted in terms of solar attraction.

A sweeping simplification was thus successfully achieved; the concepts of gravitation and acceleration thus united in the theory made it possible to predict many diverse phenomena. Even our present knowledge that there can be significant deviations from Newtonian theory under extreme conditions cannot greatly diminish the excellence of a theory at once so comprehensive and precise, yet so simple and comparatively accurate. The prediction of the existence of the planet Neptune (p. 39) is perhaps its most spectacular triumph.

Another illustration of the interest and importance of testing concerns Darwin's theory of 1842 that coral islands and atolls were formed through subsidence of mountains over geological time. To prove this, deep borings are essential. As may be seen from Fig. 1.6, on the subsidence theory a bore made on an atoll should reveal a thick cap of limestone, formed from dead coral organisms. Since the latter cannot live at depths greater than about 120 feet, a very thick limestone cap is direct confirmation of the theory of slow subsidence. The theory was not adequately tested until 1952, when, at Eniwetok atoll, two borings were made (Ladd *et al.*) to the great depths of 4222 and 4630 feet. Only near the bottom of each deep bore did the limestone from dead corals give way to volcanic basalt rock. This demonstration of the existence of a vast thick cap of limestone was striking confirmation of the subsidence theory: the rock was the summit of an extinct volcano rising two miles above the ocean floor.

More commonly associated with Charles Darwin's name is his theory of evolution, which implies that species of plants and animals change perceptibly with the passage of time. This idea, however, was by no means new; indeed, in Professor Waddington's words "The Greek philosophers, who thought of almost every notion which mankind has been able to conceive, certainly thought of this one [evolution] too; but in their usual way they tasted it, and sniffed at it, but never really tested it by experiment or detailed observation."

In his book of 1859 entitled "On the Origin of Species", Darwin approached his subject scientifically; his idea of evolution was open to detailed testing, and he himself cited many observations which elegantly fitted into his unifying scheme. He also postulated a plausible mechanism by which evolution occurred. Since the individuals in any given species vary among themselves, then, if these variations are inherited by succeeding generations, the variants most fitted to their environment will tend to survive at the expense of those less well suited.

Qualitatively, Darwin's theory was consistent with the data, but was it in quantitative agreement? In other words, are the variations sufficiently pronounced and sufficiently frequent to explain the transformation of one species into another? Quantitative experiments are clearly required; they are more difficult to carry out, but they are much sharper and more elegant tests of a theory than is qualitative observations. Random mutations are now known to occur spontaneously, and agents such as X-rays or certain chemicals can increase the frequency of mutation. One well-known natural mutation in recent times has been that of the light-coloured moth *Biston betularia* which has, in the past half-century, evolved a black form that is much less conspicuous against dark surfaces. It has thereby survived the predatory attacks of birds in the soot-blackened industrial Midlands of England. This is a clear confirmation of Darwin's theory of "the survival of the fittest".

Artificial mutations are often more drastic and more disadvantageous than this. Professor Waddington found that if he treated the eggs of the fruit-fly *Drosophila* with ether vapour, some of the flies developed a rudimentary extra wing. After many generations of appropriate selection of these altered flies, he obtained a strain in which most individuals inherited quite a good extra pair of wings. That mutations such as these are observed to occur so readily suggests that, over geological time, evolution could well have led to the formation of the species as we know them today. Thus has Darwin's theory of evolution successfully stood up to practical tests.

Other illustrations of how essential are experiments, come from ancient Greece. Democritus, who flourished about 420 B.C., propounded the theory that matter is composed of indestructible atoms, which are physically indivisible, and between which there is empty space. This theory was put forward to explain, comprehensively but in simple terms the properties of heat, light and smell. Applying the theory to the latter subject, Lucretius (*c.* 47 B.C.) wrote as follows.

"You cannot suppose that atoms of the same shape are entering our nostrils when stinking corpses are roasting as when the stage is freshly sprinkled with saffron of Cilicia and a nearby altar exhales the perfumes of the Orient.... You may readily infer that such substances as agreeably titillate the senses are composed of smooth round atoms. Those that seem bitter and harsh are more tightly compacted of hooked particles and accordingly tear their way into our senses and rend our bodies by their inroads."

Though modern research has strikingly confirmed this theory that olfaction depends on the transfer of atoms (or rather molecules) of different shapes and degrees of interaction, two thousand years elapsed before this came about. During this time, literally no progress was made in the theory of olfaction; the atomic theory of Democritus, though mildly satisfying intellectually on account of the unification it introduced, was sterile in that predictions and the appropriate experimental tests were not made.

Epicurus (who flourished about 300 B.C.) had no interest in science on its own account; he valued it solely for providing a naturalistic explanation of phenomena which superstition was attributing to the agency of the gods. If there were several possible naturalistic explanations, Epicurus held that there was no point in trying to decide between them. The Epicureans accordingly contributed practically nothing to science.

It was the prevalence of such attitudes, rather than the limited technical resources, that were responsible for this sterility; predictions suitable for testing did not follow the formulation of the theory. For example, it can be deduced from the atomic theory of matter that an oil film, spread on the surface of water, should not be capable of being thinned indefinitely; ultimately one should reach atomic (or molecular) dimensions.

The experiment to test this prediction is simple enough; many oils spread readily over the surface of water, as has been known at least from the dawn of written history. The first record seems to be a cuneiform inscription, about 4000 years old, found in the ruins of ancient Babylon. It describes in detail how the priests would tell fortunes by dropping a little sesame oil on to a water surface, looking at the colours and movements of the oil on the surface against the light of the rising sun. The changing patterns and shapes of the patches of

Fig. 2.3. Thin oil films, only a single molecule in thickness, can drastically calm the waves on wind-ruffled water. This photograph was taken during experiments at Loch Laggan, Scotland, and is reproduced by courtesy of Price's (Bromborough) Ltd.

oil were believed to indicate the future course of public and private affairs.

The ancient Greeks were more practical; they learned that certain oils, spread over water, calmed the waves thereon, as in Fig. 2.3. They too, might have predicted, and confirmed by observation, that according to the atomic theory of matter, such an oil film should not be capable of being thinned indefinitely. The experiment, however, was not made till over two thousand years later, when Benjamin Franklin (in 1765) observed that olive oil spreads over the surface of water to a limiting thickness. Even then the significance of the result in relation to the atomic theory was not appreciated. Franklin wrote: "Recollecting what I had formerly read in Pliny, I resolved to make some experiments of the effect of oil on water, when I should have the opportunity.... At length, being at Clapham (London), where there is, on the common, a large pond, which I observed one day to be very rough with the wind, I fetched out a cruet of oil, and dropped a little of it on the water. I saw it spread itself with surprising swiftness upon the surface; but the effect of smoothing the waves was not produced; for I had applied it first on the leeward side of the pond, where the waves were greatest; and the wind drove my oil back upon the shore. I then went to the windward side where they began to form; and there the oil, though not more than a teaspoonful, produced an instant calm over a space several yards square, which spread amazingly, and extended itself gradually till it reached the lee side, making all that quarter of the pond, perhaps half an acre, as smooth as a looking-glass."

The teaspoonful of oil, spread over half an acre, would be thinned to 13×10^{-8} cm (one twenty-millionth of an inch); and that the oil does not spread further, to give a still thinner film, shows that this figure is the length of the individual molecules of which it is composed. Incidentally, the result is in good accord, considering the roughness of Franklin's measurement, with modern determinations. Such an experiment could have been an early triumph for the atomic theory of matter, but it was not until Lord Rayleigh's studies of 1899 that it was taken as a direct confirmation of the theory that matter must be regarded as discontinuous.

A further example is furnished by the theory that the earth is spherical in shape (and not flat). This idea is of very great antiquity; it is usually held that Pythagoras (who flourished about 532 B.C.) was the first to formulate the theory, which Bertrand Russell supposes was congenial to Pythagoras on aesthetic grounds: the avoidance of edges and the simplicity and symmetry of the sphere may have been attractive to him. Anaxagoras (c. 460 B.C.) still maintained that the earth was flat, but the triumph of the spherical earth theory was close at hand; observation of the shape of the earth's shadow on the moon when the latter was eclipsed gave clear accord with what was to be expected on the theory of a spherical earth. The practical interest in navigation at sea kept the theory alive and vigorous. In the first half of the third century B.C., the Greek philosopher Bion used the theory of the spherical earth to predict the midnight sun in the Arctic Circle, where no ships had yet penetrated; and Eratosthenes (about 240 B.C.) studied quantitatively, from the different angles of the noon sun at Alexandria and Syene, the curvature of the earth, as in Fig. 2.4. His measurements led

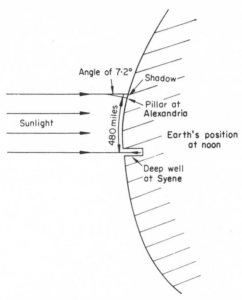

FIG. 2.4. Basis of experiment of Eratosthenes for studying the curvature of the earth. At noon, the midsummer sun at Syene (near Aswan in Egypt) is exactly vertical, its reflection being visible in the water of a deep well. But on the same day the noon sun at Alexandria, 480 miles to the north, is 7·2° away from the vertical, as deduced from the length of the shadow of a pillar. The circumference of the world, assuming it to be spherical, is thus $\left(480 \times \dfrac{360}{7·2}\right)$ miles, i.e. 24,000 miles.

to the conclusion that the circumference of the earth was 24,000 miles, which implied that men could conceivably sail right round; though this was not experimentally borne out for seventeen hundred years, when the men of Magellan's expedition first circumnavigated the earth. Incidentally, the calculated circumference of 24,000 miles is remarkably close to the modern figure of 24,860 miles.

This example shows clearly not only the interest and fertility of the "prediction–experimental test" approach; the theory of the curvature of the earth, with the various predictions deduced from it, was a scientific theory in that observational tests could provide a "yes" or "no" check on these predictions.

A particularly striking example relates to the confirmation of Einstein's theory of relativity, so well described by Popper (1963) in the following words: "Einstein's gravitational theory had led to the result that light was attracted by heavy bodies (such as the sun), precisely as material bodies were attracted. As a consequence, it could be calculated that light from a distant fixed star whose apparent position was close to the sun would reach the earth from such a direction that the star would seem to be slightly shifted away from the sun; or, in other words, that stars close to the sun would look as if they had moved a little away from the sun, and from one another. This is a thing which cannot normally be observed since such stars are rendered invisible in daytime by the sun's overwhelming brightness; but during an eclipse it is possible to take photographs of them. If the same constellation is photographed at night one can measure the distances

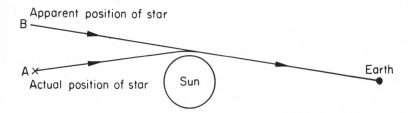

FIG. 2.5. According to the theory of relativity, light is attracted by a heavy body (such as the sun), i.e. it is bent towards such a body. Thus when the sun is in such a position that light from a distant star has to pass close to it to reach the earth, the light rays are predicted (according to this theory) to be deflected so that the star appears to be at B instead of at A.

on the two photographs, and check the predicted effect... We all—the small circle of students to which I belonged—were thrilled with the result of the eclipse observation which in 1919 brought the first important confirmation of Einstein's theory of gravitation. It was a great experience for us, and one which had a lasting influence on my intellectual development."

The confirmation, moreover, was not only qualitative (finding that the effect was significant); it was also quantitative. Einstein had predicted by his calculations that light (from a distant star) which just grazed the edge of the sun's disk should be bent by 1·745″. The experimental values obtained in 1919 were $1.61 \pm .30''$ and $1.98 \pm 0.12''$, and later values were even closer to the theoretical prediction.

A final example is taken from the works of Eddington. In his "Relativity Theory of Protons and Electrons" (published in 1936) he deduced from his theoretical equations the allegedly *a priori* knowledge that the ratio of the mass of the proton to the mass of the electron should be 1847·6. The value based on experiment, however, is rather lower; it is 1836·56, and the discrepancy is well outside the possible error of ± 0.56 claimed by the experimentalists. Which value was really more accurate, the theoretical or the experimental?

The answer to the question can best be deduced from the historical course of events. Eddington introduced a small correction, because, he said, the identification of the mass of a particle had not been quite correct in the simple theory. This correction brought the theoretical value down to 1834·1, closer to the experimental figure but by no means in exact agreement with it. However, in his "Fundamental Theory", published in 1946, Eddington pointed out that a second correction factor, namely $(137/136)^{5/6}$, had unfortunately been omitted from the earlier theoretical treatments; and that this new factor brought the calculated value to 1836·34, identical with the experimental figure within the admitted limits of error of the latter.

One may note here the unscientific features of Eddington's theory: how difficult it is to conceive of possibly refuting it, in that any wrong predictions could presumably be corrected in the same way (at the expense of the simplicity of the theory), and also in that it did not *predict*, ahead of experiment, the mass-ratio or the existence of the proton and the electron. Indeed, that the discoveries and detailed experimental studies of electrons and protons had already been carried out before the theory was formulated makes nonsense of any claim of *a priori* knowledge here; the experiments were essential in practice, as well as on logical grounds.

THE MOTIVATION FOR EXPERIMENTING

That experiments are required for logical reasons is not a strong motivation, however, the testing of a theory must also be interesting to make worthwhile the labour, often tedious, which is involved. The interest of science lies in the subtle blending of theory and experiment. Scientific theories are rather like living creatures; they may excite our curiosity, they may be useful, occasionally they are beautiful. Indeed, though they may be most *useful* (perhaps in great enterprises) when they are mature, they are often most *attractive* when they are new and still growing, i.e. when they are ranging over ever-widening fields, unifying more and more experience. Testing these wider applications is particularly exciting in that one is not sure what one will find; it also leads to personal prestige. With wonder and a desire for prestige among our motives, we predict as precisely as possible from our theory what should happen in some new experiment, and while carrying out the appropriate experimental test we are usually hoping desperately that the theory *will* work. The moment of triumph which is ours if our theory has predicted some new phenomenon accurately for the first time is one of the supreme rewards of science; and to the triumph of success is added the aesthetic pleasure in contemplating the simplification and unification successfully achieved: the joy of seeing a pattern relating hitherto disparate happenings. The confirmation of Einstein's theory of relativity in 1919 is a good example of such a triumph; another, which is more recent, relates to the prediction by Ne'eman and Gell-Mann from a general quantum-methanical theory of sub-atomic particles that there should be a new particle in atomic physics, having a negative electrical charge and a mass of about 3280 electrons. This postulated particle was named the omega-minus. Its predicted lifetime was exceedingly short, only one ten-billionth of a second; clearly its detection would not be easy. But to test the theory was tremendously important: if the theory "worked", a splendid new unification of particle physics would have been achieved.

To find whether such a particle existed at all, elaborate experiments were undertaken at Brookhaven, Long Island. Known particles (called K mesons) were allowed to enter a liquid-hydrogen bubble chamber, and the resulting tracks were photographed. At last, after the anxious analysis of 100,000 track photographs, patience was amply rewarded; two of the photographs showed particle tracks which branched and curved just as predicted for those of the omega-minus particle. The lifetime was indeed one ten-billionth of a second, and from its tracks, the omega-minus particle was found to have a mass of (3300 ± 24) electrons, an almost uncanny triumph for the theory.

On the other hand, if the theory is not ours but that of our scientific rival (it is more politely known as a "rival theory"), there is, added to our own curiosity in setting up the experiments to test it, our sense of rivalry. We now plan and carry out the experiments hoping to *disprove* this theory; similarly, our rival is planning to try to disprove our theory. Attempting to disprove (or kill) theories in this way is a very important part of scientific endeavour, rather like the role of the Opposition party in government. By carrying out such tests, stupid ideas are quickly eliminated from the field. A common interest of many observers in the same phenomenon is necessary to the growth of science; some new theories are refuted, others, after repeated testing, are accepted.

Any scientific theory is in danger of sudden death by refutation. However, death from extinction may also occur by the evolution of some more efficient theory—one which is simpler, more precise or more general.

In his writings, from 1933 onwards, Popper has rightly emphasized the importance of falsifiability; it must be conceivable that theoretical predictions might be refuted by experimental results; but Popper has carried the argument one stage further. He writes "the fact that all tests of a theory are attempted falsifications of predictions derived with its help, furnishes the clue to scientific method" (Popper, 1945, 1962). And "Every genuine *test* of a theory is an attempt to falsify it, or to refute it" (Popper, 1963). The present writer, however, takes the view that, while such attempts can be important when a rival's theory is under test, a more positive approach is required to explain the feelings and motives of a scientist when he looks for a result which, he anxiously hopes, will *confirm* the prediction of his own (or his chosen) theory. This will be considered in more detail in the next chapter.

SUMMARY

In this chapter we have seen that experiments are always necessary to test general scientific theories. To some extent the latter are *a priori* ideas; but *a priori* knowledge (of observational results) is not possible.

The spectacular eruption of scientific activity early in the seventeenth century was due to a threefold coincidence: there was, following the Renaissance, a renewed interest in the Greek mathematical traditions; there was also the Reformation, reflecting an anti-authoritarian approach to ideas and freer critical discussions; and thirdly there was a great expansion of trade, and of crafts embracing technology which, by the early seventeenth century, had made possible more accurate clocks and optical equipment. From the time of this coincidence, the eruption has continued unabated. Scientific theories were those that were testable, and new theories (e.g. of the refraction of light) in turn led to better instruments to carry out experimental tests.

Theories are thus catalysts for new instruments, and the new instruments make possible the testing of new, exciting theories. This mutually advantageous relationship has led on to today's new tools (such as linear accelerators, electron microscopes and field-ion microscopes (cf. Figs. 5.5 to 5.9)) to test the latest far-ranging yet precise theoretical predictions.

Chapter 3

Confirmation and Confidence

WHEN IS A THEORY "SCIENTIFIC"?

If any general theory is to be classed as "scientific", it must first relate a wide enough range of phenomena to be interesting. Secondly, it must make predictions, and these predictions must have a logical symmetry, in that while certain logically possible observational results would be compatible with the prediction, others would be incompatible. A clear "yes" or "no" answer is required; the theory must be capable of predicting sufficiently precisely for conceivable disproof while also being general enough (in unifying diverse phenomena) to be interesting and satisfying.

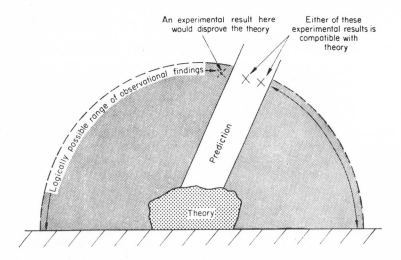

FIG. 3.1. Scientific theory and prediction from it. The experimental result may lie within the area of the prediction or may not. Thus is the theory confirmed (but never logically proved), or it is refuted. The experiment under consideration must be chosen initially so that the result might or might not be in the area of the prediction.

A theory cannot be "scientific", therefore, unless it satisfies the following two criteria: (a) predictions must be possible of what should happen (or has happened) in certain circumstances, and (b) its predictions must be sufficiently precise not to include *all* those observational results which are within the realm of logical possibility.

To illustrate these criteria I have modified and extended Popper's searchlight analogy: a searchlight is now switched on to try to track the course of a plane which is defined to be within range somewhere in the night sky. The tracking equipment may be thought of as operating automatically, being activated if, and only if, the plane is caught within the beam. The analogy (which must not be pressed too far) is illustrated in Figs. 3.1 to 3.6. In words, it runs as follows:

We study a theory and make a prediction from it,
We switch on a searchlight, and project a beam of light from it,

to test whether the experimental finding lies within the region of prediction.
to test whether the   plane   lies within the area of the beam.

The narrower this region the better; and certainly it must not be so broad
The narrower this region the better; and certainly it must not be so broad

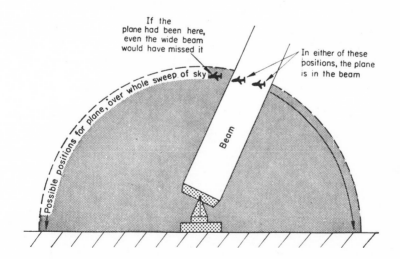

FIG. 3.2. Plane tracking analogy showing beam from searchlight flashed into a certain region of the sky. The plane may lie within the area of the beam or it may not. By definition the plane may be anywhere within range over the whole sweep of the sky.

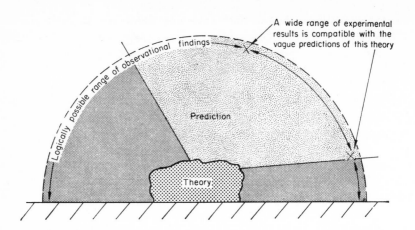

FIG. 3.3. If the prediction is very broad and vague, a wide range of possible observational results will be compatible with it. Such imprecise predictions accordingly cast but little light on the subject.

as to cover the whole logically possible range of observational findings, since this would tell us nothing new.
as to cover the whole sweep of the sky, since this would tell us nothing new.

Further, a very broad prediction is too diffuse and lacking in power
Further, a very broad   beam   is too diffuse and lacking in power

to cast much light on the subject.
to cast much light on the plane.

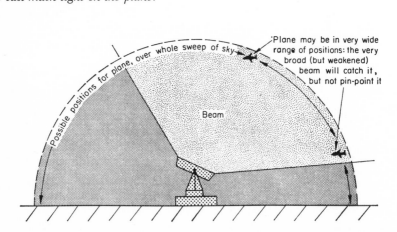

FIG. 3.4. If the beam from the searchlight is made sufficiently wide, this beam is almost sure to include the plane, but this information is of little use to the tracking mechanism.

We hope our theory will be confirmed, though we are aware it may not.
We hope the beam will fall right on target, though we are aware it may not.

The more precise the prediction, the greater will be our triumph
The narrower   the   beam,   the greater will be our triumph

if the experimental finding does lie within the theoretical prediction.
if the   plane   does lie within the beam.

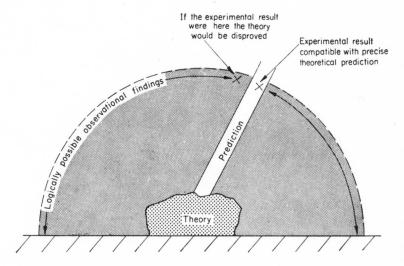

FIG. 3.5. The narrower (more precise) the prediction from theory, the greater is the triumph of confirmation.

But if after the prediction has been made, it is found to be not
But if after the   beam   has been flashed, it is found to be not

confirmed, we must examine critically the basic assumptions of the theory:
on target, we must examine critically the setting of the searchlight:

it may perhaps be possible to adjust the theory so that it is confirmed.
it may perhaps be possible to adjust the   light   so it shines full on the target.

We must, however, make sure that the adjusted theory is not imprecise, and
                                        that it is not logically loose:
*We   must,   however,   make   sure   that   the   adjusted   searchlight   is   not
                giving a very broad beam, and that it is not loose:*

the procedure of adjustment carries with it the danger that the predictions
the procedure of adjustment carries with it the danger that the searchlight

may become so loose that they cover the whole realm of possibility,
may become so loose that it swings all over the sky,

so being of no use in carrying out critical experimental tests.
so being of no use in tracking the plane.

If after we have studied the theory, it is not possible to make any
prediction from it,
If after we have switched on the searchlight, it is not possible to obtain a
beam of light from it,

this particular theory should be reconstructed or abandoned.
this particular searchlight should be reconstructed or abandoned.

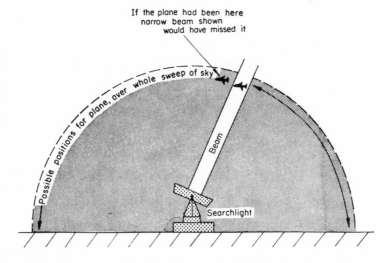

FIG. 3.6. The narrower the beam flashed from the searchlight, the greater the triumph if the plane lies within the beam.

Examples of scientific theories which are *precise* are relativity theory, the first and second laws of thermodynamics, the exponential time decay of radioactivity, and the indestructibility of atoms during chemical and physical changes. Also precise are Newton's theory of gravitation, the ideal gas theory, and the theory of the conservation of mass in chemical changes. Though they are not strictly *accurate*, we often use these theories as good enough approximations in everyday life.

Less precise is the non-quantitative theory that "evolution rates are significant", and less precise still (corresponding to the rather broad beam of light) are theories of how weather patterns change; this is too complicated for really precise forecasts of local conditions to be possible at present. "Scattered showers may occur during the next few days" is an example; here the prediction is deliberately made rather broad so that our confidence in the theory is not reduced to such an extent that we ignore the forecast in favour of some suspiciously simple, but often correct, prediction such as "tomorrow's weather will resemble today's".

Corresponding to the searchlight beam being so wide as to be diffused over the whole sky, are theories from which the predictions are so vague and diffuse that refutation becomes impossible. Many astrological predictions are in this category; the predictions can often be worded so vaguely (e.g. "you should beware of a tall dark stranger") that they are bound to be borne out by experience. Such theories are useless and uninteresting.

Adjusting the theory to fit the facts after some particular prediction has proved wrong is both inelegant and dangerous to the prestige of the theory; there is always the suspicion that the latter may be sufficiently adjustable to "explain" the *whole range* of possible results (the loose searchlight). The confidence we can place in such theories is greatly lessened by this ready adjustability. When Eddington adjusted his refuted prediction of $1847 \cdot 6$ for the ratio of the masses of the proton and the electron to the new value of $1836 \cdot 34$ the whole theory became suspect. Another example, analysed in detail by Popper, concerns the Marxist theory of history; in its earlier formulations the predictions (e.g. of the character of the coming social revolution) were testable and were in fact falsified by later historical events (see p. 89). The theory was then made more adjustable with auxiliary hypotheses, losing precision and prestige in the process.

As examples of theories which are unscientific, in that they allow of no predictions, are various vague psychoanalytical theories about the human mind, particularly those concerned with the interpretation of dreams. It is as if the searchlight is faulty in being so opaque or so complicated as to be unworkable, so that it emits no beam. A decision as to which of several rival theories (searchlights) is to be preferred then rests only on the relative unification achieved by each theory, and on its simplicity and elegance. After reconstruction, however, such theories may well become scientific; and Professor K. M. Colby's experiments with an electronic computer are in this direction. He programmed a patient's neurosis into an IBM 7090 computer, giving it (in code) the anxieties and decisions towards men of a single woman patient. This "pseudo-patient" then had a vocabulary of 257 words and 105 beliefs. From the interaction of these beliefs—some of which can be in conflict with others—one can then predict from the "pseudo-patient" what the resultant course of action in certain circumstances would be.

DISCREPANCIES BETWEEN THEORETICAL PREDICTIONS AND OBSERVATIONAL RESULTS

If there is lack of agreement between theory and experiment it may be that *the experimental result is not being correctly interpreted*. For example, it has often been claimed in recent years that porpoises can swim faster than should be physically possible from a knowledge of their muscular horsepower and the shape that has to be propelled through the sea. The disagreement was widely interpreted as indicating that the shape factor used in the theory must be wrong, and that the porpoise when swimming must change its shape somewhat, so as to disturb the water as little as possible. It now appears, however, that the quoted swimming speeds referred to porpoises riding (surfing) on the bow waves of the ships from which the observations were made. Without the benefit of this bow wave the porpoise swims at a velocity compatible with the usual theoretical predictions.

A second example concerns the density of nitrogen. In 1894 Ramsay took up the problem which Cavendish had raised a century earlier, that though according to the existing atomic theory the element nitrogen should be the same whether obtained as a residual gas from the air (after removal of the oxygen and carbon dioxide) or by the decomposition of nitrates, yet in practice the nitrogen from the air always appeared to be about 0·5% denser. This discrepancy between theory and experiment finally led Ramsay to propose that the nitrogen obtained from the air contained traces of some inert heavier gas. This new theory was strikingly confirmed by his subsequent experiment of reacting the nitrogen from the air with magnesium, leaving a residue (about 1%) of a new and very inert gas, which he called argon. Under the stimulus of this discovery a whole family of these rare gases was discovered in the succeeding years.

If, however, there is lack of agreement between theory and experiment when we are, as far as we can see, measuring the required effect, then *the theoretical prediction must have been in error*. Even so, the test may well have been useful in that we had to refer back to our fundamental assumptions in the theory. A critical examination of these may show that they were completely erroneous (as in Eddington's theory above) or that we had neglected some not insignificant factor, or that we had perhaps assumed a boundary condition which was itself erroneous. The testing thus constitutes the "sympathetic understanding of experience", from which we may go on to propose a new and (we hope) better theory.

For example Galileo, pondering over a lift-pump that would not pump water from a depth greater than about 30 feet, concluded at first that the pump must be faulty; for the theory of pump action (held from the time of Aristotle) was that "nature abhors a vacuum", and as Galileo remarked, there was no obvious reason that this abhorrence should suddenly stop short at heights greater than 30 feet above the water. Further investigation, however, showed that the pump was *not* faulty; indeed it was common knowledge among miners that a relay of lift pumps, each operating a stage of about 30 feet, was always required to pump out a deep mine. The current theory of pump action (that "nature abhors a vacuum") was thus refuted. A new theory, that the weight or pressure of the atmosphere *pushes* the water up was then developed by Galileo and his pupil Torricelli. From this new theory one could also make a new prediction, that the weight of the atmospheric air could be balanced by a column of mercury about 30 inches high, as was confirmed by Torricelli's experiment of 1643, which involved the construction of the first barometer.

The discovery of a new planet must surely be among the most spectacular results of disagreement between theory and experiment. In 1846 the French astronomer Leverrier, studying the perturbations of the path of the planet Uranus, found that these did not fit exactly with predictions from the Newtonian theory of gravitational interactions with the other known planets. He then modified the theory to include an additional Newtonian interaction; this was of such a magnitude as would come from an undetected planet in a certain stated position in the sky. This prediction was strikingly confirmed in the same year; the astronomer Galle, searching carefully the region of the sky close to the predicted position, found a new planet, which was named Neptune, situated within one degree of the position calculated by Leverrier. Our plane-tracking analogy (Figs. 3.2, 3.4 and 3.6) might thus be modified to include planet-tracking!

A final example of a new and better theory following the refutation of the old concerns the physical ether. The fact that light waves, gravitational attraction and magnetic attraction can all pass through apparently empty space led many scientists, including Newton, to theorize that, even in the absence of ordinary matter, space contains an elastic medium, which was called the physical ether. To test this theory, Michelson and Morley made a calculated prediction of how far the apparent velocity of light (in the alleged ether) should be different along, and transverse to, the direction of the earth's orbital motion (through the ether). Although their measurements of 1887, and those of subsequent investigators, showed *no* significant difference in the velocity of light in these two directions, this lack of agreement with existing theory was shortly to prove highly fruitful in stimulating the development of the theory of relativity.

ATTRIBUTES OF A SCIENTIFIC THEORY

Any scientific theory can be characterized by the following attributes:

(a) *The range of experience* incorporated into the theory, i.e. the unification of intellectual concepts which is achieved. The greater the unification, the more *"fundamental"* the theory is said to be. This is discussed again on p. 59.

(b) *Its simplicity.* This term is discussed in detail in Chapter 5.

(c) *The precision* of the predictions that can be made from it. If the theory predicts that some experimental variable x equals A under certain conditions, it is highly *precise* (though maybe not right). In descending order of precision, for example, are the predictions: $x = A$; $B > x > A$; $x > A$; x is significant; some x may occur in the next few days.

(d) *Its "testedness"*, i.e. its having been tested repeatedly in various ways over a wide range of experimental conditions.

(e) The *proportion of refutations* it has suffered during this testing. It may have a reputation for yielding more or less inaccurate predictions.

The overall regard we have for some particular theory depends on why we are interested in it, as well as on the relative importance in the theory of these five factors.

If it is *confidence and credibility* we require (as with the theories behind engineering design, or weather forecasting), there is an *inverse* relationship with attributes (a), (b) and (c); in that the wider the intellectual range, the simpler the theory, and the more precise the prediction, the less confidence we feel in the prediction being confirmed by observation or experiment. It is rather as if we were asked to bet that "this horse will win all its races by at least one second". Reducing the range of experience and the precision, however, can increase our confidence and credibility; we might now, on our racing analogy, be betting that in one of its races the horse will be placed. If the horse has already an unbroken record of wins under various conditions we shall be more encouraged to bet on a further win than if he has never run before or has had some failures. Similarly, repeated confirmations of a theory over a wide range of conditions inspire confidence, whereas lack of testing, or known refutations, reduce our confidence in it. Confidence therefore requires (d) to be high but (e) to be low.

If, however, we require intellectual *excellence* in a theory, as indicated by the intellectual interest and excitement it generates, then attributes (a), (b) and (c) must all be great, while refutations (e) should be zero after extensive testing (d). Such excellent theories are sometimes called "laws". In popular use, the word "hypothesis" is applied to a relatively untested theory of a small range, i.e. to a theory of low excellence. If the content of (a) is still lower, we have an ordinary generalization, such as the dog's "there is always a cat in that driveway".

The attributes of excellence, confidence and credibility can be illustrated by comparing Newton's theoretical treatment of motion with Einstein's relativity theory of 1905. Newton's theory, which had reigned virtually unchallenged from 1686, unified gravity and acceleration; it was certainly fundamental. It was also agreeably simple; it made very precise predictions, and until the present century had not suffered any refutations in spite of most extensive testing. Indeed, the accuracy of this theory is usually so satisfactory that it remains in general use today. Most scientists would agree that this is an *excellent* theory; its simplicity offsets the minor refutations (on grounds of accuracy) which it has suffered, but the latter do detract from the confidence we feel in using it in completely new situations.

Einstein's theory of relativity, on the other hand, is also an *excellent* theory; it has the advantage over Newton's of unifying an additional phenomenon, namely light, though this is achieved at the expense of simplicity. Further, it is also very precise, and it has predicted accurately (without even minor refutations) various interactions, including two effects that a gravitational field has on light, where the latter is changed in frequency and is also deflected (this effect has been discussed in Chapter 2). Another prediction concerns the velocity of light or radio waves. Relativity theory predicts quantitatively an (exceedingly small) decrease of velocity when light passes through a strong gravitational field. At the time of writing (1965), Dr. I. I. Shapiro at M.I.T. was planning a suitable experimental test. This involved measuring the time which electromagnetic microwaves take to reach the planet Venus and bounce back to the earth, firstly when the position of the planet is away from the sun, and secondly when

Venus lies so nearly behind the sun that the microwaves have to pass through the intense gravitational field near the surface of the sun. Relativity theory makes the precise prediction that, if they pass near the sun, the microwaves should be retarded by 0·0002 second. But since the round trip time of the microwaves is about 25 minutes, extremely accurate instrumentation is clearly required. Confirmation would be a triumph not only for relativity theory but also for modern instrument technology.

SUMMARY

Scientific theories must allow predictions, and are most interesting (and the confirmations are a greater triumph) when they are most precise. Certainly the predictions must be sufficiently precise not to include *all* the observational results which are within the realms of logical possibility. If the predictions (or "explanations") are so vague that they *do* include all such results, then the theories cannot be regarded as scientific.

Theories which can easily be suitably adjusted if the predictions are refuted are regarded with reduced confidence, and theories which make no predictions whatsoever we do not classify as scientific theories.

The *confidence* we feel in a theory varies inversely with attributes (a), (b), (c) and (e) on p. 40, but directly with attribute (d). The *excellence* of a theory, on the other hand, is directly proportional to attributes (a), (b), (c) and (d), while (e) must be close to, and preferably equal to, zero.

Chapter 4

Engineering and Science

THEORIES AND THE ENGINEER

It has often been maintained that engineers proceed rather differently from scientists. For example Popper (1945, 1962) writes that in scientific method all tests of a theory are attempted falsifications of predictions derived with its help, but that "in the case of applied sciences, our interest is different. The engineer who uses physics in order to build a bridge is predominantly interested in a prognosis: whether or not a bridge of a certain kind described (by the initial conditions) will carry a certain load."

But the *origin* of theories shows no distinction between science and engineering, as the following example shows. In May 1765, James Watt evolved the theory of the steam engine. He had already been studying the Newcomen engine, and had made experiments on the relation between the pressure and temperature of steam, so that it was from this background that the leap of the imagination occurred. He described the occasion as follows. "It was in the Green of Glasgow. I had gone to take a walk on a fine Sabbath afternoon. I had entered the Green by the gate at the foot of Charlotte Street—had passed the old washing house. I was thinking on the engine...and gone as far as the Herd's House, when the idea came into my mind that as steam was an elastic body it would rush into a vacuum, and if a communication was made between the cylinder and an exhausted vessel, it would rush into it and might be there condensed without cooling the cylinder....I had not walked further than the Golf house when the whole thing was arranged in my mind." This account may be compared with those in Chapter 1; it shows that there is no distinction to be made between the *origins* of scientific and of engineering theories.

Moreover, if we now consider the *testing* of theories, and if (on the basis of Chapter 3) we accept that the pure scientist is often attempting to *confirm* his theory over as wide a range of variables as possible (even though the theory may conceivably be disproved by the experimental findings), any basic philosophical difference between the approaches of

43

the scientist and the engineer disappears. For example, when the engineer plans to construct a bridge or a dam across a river he must invoke theories about the strengths, creep and possible fatigue of his constructional materials, about the stability of the ground on either side, about the maximum expected rate of flow of the river, about expected earth tremors, wind speeds, and so on. He will doubtless make experiments to test these theories over a moderate range, studying a model of the bridge or dam and examining the ground for geological faults. He then builds the dam or bridge, hoping ardently that his theoretical predictions about the stability of the full-scale structure over very long periods of time and the permissible loadings will be confirmed. The engineer has here a philosophical outlook very similar to that of a scientist who is looking for and hoping for confirmation of his theory (such as the physicist's confirmation of the theory of relativity mentioned on p. 28, or a chemist's synthesis of some new material).

The *scale* of the operation influences, to some extent, whether it is called science or engineering. The production of the atomic bomb illustrates this point. Basic studies of the radioactive breakdown of small numbers of uranium (U^{235}) atoms suggested that the breakdown should proceed faster if the mass of uranium were increased, till when a certain critical mass was reached, the breakdown should become explosively fast. Whether to call the testing of this prediction physics or engineering is only a matter of terminology; much more significant was the confirmation of the theory. However, since the critical mass of uranium was of the order of a kilogram, the experiment was regarded as in the province of engineering. If, on the other hand, the critical mass of some other fissile material were in the microgram range, experiments with this critical mass would be in the realm of physics.

This example shows that there is no sharp logical distinction between engineering and pure science, and that such differences as there are concern emphasis, motives and the scale of the operation. Even the latter is not very significant; scaling-up from laboratory physics or chemistry to full-scale engineering (by a linear factor of perhaps 100 times) involves a range much smaller than is customary in physical and chemical theory, where, for example, the idea of atoms behaving like little hard billiard balls involves a scaling factor of about a hundred million times.

STRATEGY IN ENGINEERING

Besides differences in the scale of their operations, there can be different motives for theorizing and experimenting between engineers and pure scientists. For the pure scientist, the motives are usually curiosity and a desire to see a simplifying pattern relating hitherto disconnected phenomena. The motive of the engineer, on the other hand, is to make something to operate satisfactorily. However, differences of scale and motive are neither in the realm of logic nor of the philosophy of science, except in one respect: the engineer may have less choice than the pure scientist in the system to be studied. Many useful and important engineering processes involve very complex materials, including mixtures containing many components and liquids with non-Newtonian flow properties. To deal quantitatively with these systems so that the effects of variations can be precisely predicted, the engineer needs to alter as many of the variables as widely as possible. Preferably this is done by studying them one at a time, though often this procedure is not physically possible. For example, the high pressures and the high temperatures induced when a shock-wave hits a solid or a liquid both may cause changes which are extremely difficult to separate.

Often, in dealing with a complicated practical situation, the engineer arbitrarily reduces the number of variables in his theory by combining certain of them into dimensionless groups, of which a well-known example is the Reynolds number of a fluid flowing through a pipe. It is defined as (flow-rate × density × pipe diameter/viscosity). If this group exceeds about 2000 in many systems, the flow of the fluid changes from being smooth (laminar), to being turbulent. Such dimensionless groups are evaluated in the laboratory, and are then used for predicting the behaviour in a large-scale chemical plant. But this procedure reduces somewhat our confidence in our predictions, though the group as a whole may have varied widely in the laboratory experiments; one or more of the variables within the group may have been virtually unchanged. Because of this reduced confidence in using dimensionless groups in "scaling-up" predictions, the chemical engineer usually builds a pilot plant, intermediate in size between the laboratory system and the proposed full-scale production plant, so that he can check whether the "scaling-up" predictions of his simplified theory are "working" sufficiently accurately.

If, however, the chemical engineer *can* evaluate his variables separately (i.e. can "go basic"), thus putting forward a sufficiently complex but nevertheless precise theory to predict the behaviour of his complicated practical system, he can eliminate the pilot-plant stage, proceeding to scale-up directly from laboratory studies to the design and construction of the full-scale production plant. This saves considerable expense and time. The reduced simplicity of this theoretical approach

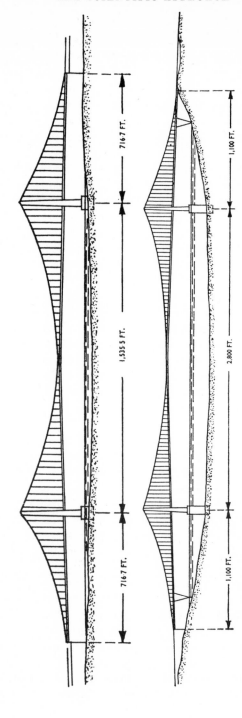

Fig. 4.1(a). Philadelphia-Camden (1926) and Tacoma (1940) suspension bridges. A suspension bridge with relatively low towers and consequent very graceful sweep may (for the same span) be more expensive than one with taller towers.

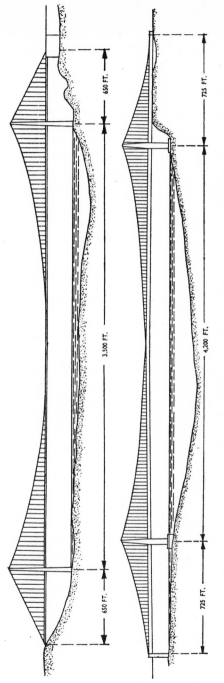

FIG. 4.1(b). Two more suspension bridges: George Washington (1931) and Golden Gate (1937).

increases the confidence we feel in the result (cf. p. 40). We should be more suspicious if a theory were rather simple when we know that in practice many factors are likely to be operative simultaneously.

In recent years the ready availability of mathematical computers to handle the algebraic calculations, the widespread use of the methods of operational research (described in Chapter 7), have made it much easier for the engineer to use more complicated mathematical correlations on which to base his predictions. This approach, sometimes termed "going fundamental", is, however, less fundamental than is a theory in physics which links hitherto unrelated concepts. The engineer is merely avoiding over-simplification. We may have considerable confidence in his computer-based predictions; though, because of their limited range and lack of simplicity, they are not necessarily of high "excellence" in the sense described on p. 41. This lack of "excellence" may, however, be compensated for by good engineering design (see below).

DESIGN IN ENGINEERING

Just as there are often several possible ways of designing a given laboratory test in pure science (e.g. in the detection of fundamental particles), so there are usually many possible ways of designing a bridge or a chemical plant. The chemical engineer, for example, designing a plant to produce a new plastic, can arrange the mixers, reactors, coolers and other pieces of equipment in various relationships one to the other and the plant will still work.

The bridge designer has also a choice of bridge designs, even for a given geological structure on each bank; especially if he is not limited to the absolute minimum cost. Aesthetics may play a part; a suspension bridge may be designed in various ways, as shown in Fig. 4.1(a) and (b). Which is preferable? Or should the bridge be of a different design altogether, as illustrated in Fig. 4.2?

It could happen, moreover, that several designs for a bridge of a certain capacity involve the same cost; the choice would then be *entirely aesthetic*, lying outside the province of science. Such an aesthetic choice in design, perhaps between several structures each elegant in its different way, can counterbalance the lower "intellectual excellence" of engineering theories as compared with those of pure science. The engineer's aesthetic choice balances the physicist's choice of simple, "fundamental" systems; design artistry can be set against intellectual artistry.

FIG. 4.2. Thomas Telford's road bridge across the Conway—"castellated" to match the Castle, and with a footbridge added alongside. On the left is the modern road bridge, on the right the tubular railway bridge. Photographed from the Castle, by C. V. Hancock, Birmingham, and reproduced by arrangement.

STRATEGY IN SCIENCE

Design and strategy in engineering have their counterpart in the strategy of approach to any scientific problem, pure or applied. Strategy is of the utmost importance. Often there are many possible ways to solve a problem, but some of them may be too complicated, laborious or expensive to be feasible.

In organic chemical syntheses, for example, there are often many possible paths leading to the required solution. In the complete crystal structure analysis of a complicated molecule, success depends to a large extent on the strategy—choosing for synthesis and X-ray diffraction analysis appropriately substituted derivatives. Of course, skilful tactics in handling both the crystals and the mathematical analysis of the X-ray diffraction patterns are essential, but much depends on the choice of which chemical substitutions are to be made in the molecule in order that the X-ray scattering from one or two isolated parts of the molecule can be clearly identified within the highly complex overall X-ray scattering pattern. Only thus, in (relatively) easy stages, can the complete molecular structure of even a very complicated molecule be deduced from the X-ray patterns. Professor Dorothy Hodgkin's prediction in this way of the chemical structure of the penicillin molecule won her a Nobel Prize.

CONFIDENCE AND CREDIBILITY

The engineer is concerned with making something that is virtually certain to operate satisfactorily. To increase as far as he can our credibility and confidence in his theories and predictions, the engineer generally avoids very precise predictions. He introduces a "safety factor" of perhaps 3 times into his designs, and the consequent improvement in credibility and confidence is attained at the expense of "intellectual excellence". In terms of the plane-tracking analogy of Chapter 3, the engineer's approach is to broaden the beam of light so that he may be more confident that the plane shall not lie outside his beam. But occasionally, as we know, a bridge or a dam does collapse. Some geological fault may perhaps be closer or more serious than the

FIG. 4.3. Tacoma Narrows Bridge in process of breaking, 1940.
(Photograph by courtesy of Associated Press.)

engineer predicted, or an earth tremor may prove more severe than he considered within the realm of reasonable possibility. Refutation of the theories of the engineer *can* thus conceivably occur, often with disastrous results (Fig. 4.3); and the smaller the safety factors (the narrower the beam) the less confidence one feels in the results. This is particularly true of spaceflight rockets, where to save weight there are necessarily drastic reductions of the usual engineering safety factors. Here, as in fundamental physics, making a prediction precise (narrowing the beam of light for plane-tracking) somewhat reduces our confidence in the result, but adds greatly to the interest and excitement of the test.

FIG. 4.4. Rocket exploding just after launching: "drastic reduction in the usual engineering safety factors". (Photograph by courtesy of Associated Press.)

SUMMARY

We have shown that there is no logical distinction between the methods of the engineer and the pure scientist; both may be concerned with confirming their theoretical predictions. Such differences as there are concern the scale of the experiment, the motives for undertaking it, and the artistry of design inherent in most engineering operations. The engineer is necessarily less able to choose simple, intellectually elegant systems, but the pleasures of making something "work", and of the aesthetic element in design, can offset this.

Engineering predictions should be such that we have great confidence in their being confirmed. Safety factors are therefore introduced, corresponding to broadening the beam in the searchlight analogy.

Chapter 5

The Simple Laws of Science

INTRODUCTION

We have seen in Chapter 1 that a scientific theory (general in extent or in time or in both) has *no* logical status; a theory may be inspiration, a leap of the imagination, an analogy or a dream. Wherever an idea originates, whether it seems obvious or trivial, brilliant or stupid, it is still a scientific theory provided that it predicts particular results which might conceivably (however difficult the experiment) either confirm or disprove it. The *value* of theory is that it suggests further observations; indeed, we *always* make our experiments or observations with some general idea (i.e. theory) of how the system might behave. At the very least we hold that a system might, in certain circumstances, behave unusually!

Not only should a scientific theory be experimentally testable, but it should also preferably be *easily* tested. With the possibility that many theories are silly and trivial it is most desirable that experiments can be carried out as easily as possible. Sir Francis Darwin relates an anecdote on this theme concerning his father, Charles Darwin.

"He often said that no one could be a good observer unless he was an active theorizer. This brings me back to what I said about his instinct for arresting exceptions: it was as though he were charged with theorizing power ready to flow into any channel on the slightest disturbance, so that no fact, however small, could avoid releasing a stream of theory, and thus the fact became magnified into importance. In this way it naturally happened that many untenable theories occurred to him; but fortunately his richness of imagination was equalled by his power of judging and condemning the thoughts that occurred to him. He was just to his theories, and did not condemn them unheard; and so it happened that he was willing to test what would seem to most people not at all worth testing. These rather wild trials he called 'fool's experiments', and enjoyed extremely. As an example I may mention that finding the seed-leaves of a kind of sensitive plant to be highly sensitive to vibrations of the table, he fancied that they might perceive the vibrations of sound, and therefore made me play my bassoon close to a plant."

SIMPLICITY

Equally important with the easy testing of theories, however, is the desirability that relatively *few* experiments should be required in each test of the theory. If it were possible to test a theory only after millions of measurements, the scientific literature would be full of wild ideas remaining to be tested. That this is not so is due to our desire for a simple theory (often, if well tested, called a "law", though logically the latter term is no more rigorous than the word "generalization"). Aesthetically, most people prefer simplicity and symmetry, and do not propose a complicated theory if they could propose a simpler one. But there is a more important argument for simple theories. If a "simple" theory is defined (Popper, 1935, 1959) as one with few arbitrary parameters, it is consequently more readily tested experimentally than is a theory involving more parameters. Thus, on this definition, the expressions $y = Ax$, $y = B \sin x$, $y = C \log (1 + x^2)$ are all equally simple in that they each contain only one arbitrary parameter (A, B, etc.) which can be adjusted to fit the experimental results. Such theoretical expressions can consequently easily be checked by further experiments.

Intuitively, however, we use the concept of simplicity somewhat more widely, and in a context which is subjective as well as numerical. Thus we think of $y = D/x^2$ as being a simpler function than $y = D/x^{1.998}$, and of $y = Ax$ being simpler than $y = C \log (1 + x^2)$, which in turn is simpler than $y = \log \tan \left(\dfrac{\pi}{4} + \dfrac{Ex}{2} \right)$. Simplicity thus includes an element of aesthetic appreciation, and for this reason it is scarcely easier to agree on a definition of "simplicity" than on one of "beauty".

In spite of this controversy, however, there are many theories and laws which are generally accepted as simple, and which have stood up to repeated testing. Or, in Einstein's words, "The most unintelligible thing about the world is that it is intelligible." Looking more closely at this problem, let us now examine first with what *accuracy* certain of these simple laws are valid experimentally; secondly how far the simplicity of the laws follows from our *conventions* in selecting the systems we study; and thirdly whether the *abundance* of simple laws is surprisingly great.

EXAMPLES OF SIMPLE LAWS

Among the "simple" laws—involving few parameters (and often but not necessarily, small, integral powers)—may be cited:

Avogadro's Law: For any substance the molecular weight in grams behaves as N separate kinetic particles in diverse phenomena. Here N is a constant, independent of the molecular weight.

Inverse Square Law: The gravitational or electrical force between two bodies varies inversely as the square of their distance apart.

Radioactivity Decay Law: The rate of radioactive disintegration of a substance is independent of its temperature, pressure or state of chemical combination.

Constancy of Mass of Electron: All electrons (or protons) have the same resting mass: negative electricity is not found in a spread of packets of various sizes.

Ohm's Law: The electrical current flowing through a body is proportional to the applied voltage.

Hooke's Law: The extension of a spring varies as the first power of the load applied (Fig. 5.1).

Gas Law: The volume of a given mass of a gas varies inversely as the pressure to which it is subjected (Fig. 5.2).

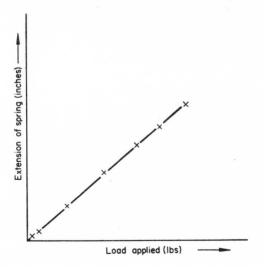

FIG. 5.1. The extension of a spring (in excess of its unloaded length) varies as the first power of the load applied (Hooke's law).

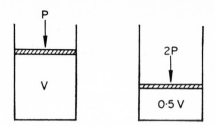

FIG. 5.2. The volume of a given mass of gas varies inversely as the pressure to which it is subjected.

Poiseuille's Law: The rate of flow of a given liquid through a tube is proportional to the pressure drop across the ends of the tube (Fig. 5.3).

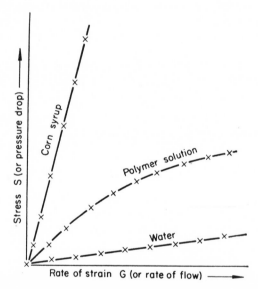

FIG. 5.3. The rate of flow of a given liquid through a tube is directly proportional to the pressure drop across the ends of the tube (Poiseuille's law). This holds for corn syrup and for water, but not for solutions of certain polymers.

Kekulé's Hypothesis: Certain organic reactions (e.g. the nitration of toluene) occur as if part of certain organic molecules consisted of a ring of six carbon atoms, this ring remaining intact during the reaction.

These simple laws correlate well the experimental data over wide ranges of variables, including different materials. The value of N, for example, is found to be $6·02 \times 10^{23}$ for materials as different as pollen grains, hydrogen gas molecules and crystalline salts. The figures for N for the latter are found from X-ray analysis. Concordant figures are also obtained from such diverse methods as comparing the viscosity and diffusion of sugar in water, and by measuring the amount of helium produced from radioactive elements.

Again, the exponent in the "inverse square law" has often been found to be exactly -2, showing that certain chosen systems approximate closely to the simple mathematical model of completely isolated point charges or masses. Such systems can be found relatively easily.

Quantitatively, one may show that any correlation can be "simple", provided that the range of variables is chosen to be sufficiently small (Hooke's law is a good example of this). In general, one may demonstrate the effect of the range of variables on the simplicity (measured by the paucity of arbitrarily adjustable parameters) by considering some function y which is altered by a change in the variable x. If the latter is increased from x_1 to $(x_1 + \Delta x)$, then Taylor's series applied to

$$y = f(x_1 + \Delta x)$$

gives

$$y = f(x_1) + \Delta x f'(x_1) + \frac{(\Delta x)^2}{2!} f''(x_1) + \frac{(\Delta x)^3}{3!} f'''(x_1) \ldots \qquad \text{(iv)}$$

or

$$y = A + B\Delta x + C(\Delta x)^2 + D(\Delta x)^3 + \ldots \qquad \text{(v)}$$

where A, B, C, etc., are constants.

This equation shows that any correlation of two variables can always be *made* simple (though at the expense of its generality or accuracy) by merely neglecting the terms involving C, D, etc. Further, for *any* given values of C, D, etc., we may always make the correlation appear simple by choosing to work over such small ranges Δx that the terms in $(\Delta x)^2$ and the higher powers may be neglected. Hence a simple (2-parameter) law of the form

$$y = A + B\Delta x \qquad \text{(vi)}$$

can always be obtained provided that the range of variables is sufficiently small. Such linear relationships (often with $A = 0$) are found between the pressure of gas in a vessel and the mass of gas pumped into that vessel, in electrochemistry, and in rheological systems. The latter may be illustrated by a typical plot (Fig. 5.3) of shear stress S against the rate of strain G in a liquid. For "Newtonian" liquids the plot is rectilinear through the origin, i.e.

$$S = \eta G \qquad \text{(vii)}$$

the constant slope η being called the viscosity of the liquid.

That this relationship holds quite accurately for many liquids, including water and alcohol, denotes that the work to make the necessary hole in the liquid for viscous flow to occur is unaffected by the flow process. This is because the molecules of alcohol or water behave as tiny, independent, hard spheres: the inter-molecular forces vary as r^{-7}, but the intra-molecular forces for such molecules vary as r^{-10}, where r is the atomic or molecular separation (see p. 60). If, however, the liquid consists of a solution of long, thread-like molecules, these may each be uncoiled relatively easily, obeying a modified Hooke's law. Such additional intra-molecular forces are of longer range and much weaker, and consequently the flow process may effect the molecular configuration. These intra-molecular effects correspond to appreciable values of C, D, etc., in eq. (v), and the viscosity η varies with the flow rate G unless this is made extremely small.

CONVENTIONS AND SIMPLE LAWS

One aspect of convention in science is that we usually test the laws by working over a rather limited range of variables. The simple gas laws have not usually been tested over enormous ranges of pressure, temperature or time. *Secondly*, we usually choose relatively simple systems to investigate in detail, particularly those in which it is possible to keep all but two of the possible variables constant during the test. Another illustration of our choosing the simplest approach is seen from the way in which we draw a continuous line through several experimental points, in order to predict intermediate values by *interpolation*. For example, if we have the experimental points

● ● ● ● ● ● ●

we usually put a line through them as simply as possible, thus

and the interpolation generally works out much better than if the line

were used instead.

Why should we have used the simplest possible mathematical symbolization, i.e. (in general nomenclature) $y = $ constant or $dy/dx = 0$?

The answer lies, of course, in the *choice* of system we have made. For example, we have seen that some inanimate object is relatively permanent; it does not usually grow and shrink before our eyes. So if we determine its weight W at different times t we feel confident in assuming that the continuous straight line through the points represents intermediate values, i.e. that $dW/dt = 0$ in general for this system.

But if we had been studying a system which we knew from prior experience was more complicated, such as the weight of a dog at different times of the day, we should *expect* to find sudden increases occurring when the animal had just been fed. Even though it is much simpler for us to do so, we should therefore hesitate to draw a straight line through the points on the graph of weight versus time, but rather would we carry out a closer series of weighings. For example, the following observations

would be interpreted in more general terms *not* as this

since, after making further observations on the animal, we might well find finally a relation like this

Thus we see that the general principle of simplicity of the formal generalizations of physics is to some extent a consequence of our prior commonsense knowledge of the easily symbolized systems of physics. Further, systems giving discontinuous plots (e.g. that of the number of uranium atoms exploding as a function of time) are said to be not completely understood, since no continuity in the process can yet be apprehended. Like Mendel's laws of inheritance, they are therefore formulated in statistical terms which though precise are not as fundamental as we should like.

Yet a *third* aspect of convention is the use of *analogy*. That arguing by analogy plays a large part in our theorizing is generally agreed, and, although without logical basis, simple analogies often correlate the physical data quite well. Spengler emphasized that we transpose concepts into physics; we speak of migrant ions, magnetic fields, flying and colliding gas molecules, electrical currents and electromagnetic waves.

Indeed, it is pleasantly surprising that so many of these simple concepts stand up so well to repeated physical tests. We "scale-down" many macroscopic concepts, and often find that they still "work" tolerably well. The concept of the molecule behaving as a minute billiard ball is a typical example of this procedure.

THE ABUNDANCE OF SIMPLE LAWS

That "scaling-down" of concepts is so often in accord with physical experience, and that in practice there are proportionately so many laws which are simple but nevertheless of considerable accuracy, is due, I believe, to the wide separation of the various groups of forces occurring in nature. These forces occur in four principal bands, ranging from very strong forces of very short range up to the much weaker long-range forces. The range of a force between two bodies is measured by the dependence of the force on the distance r between them; thus a dependence on $1/r^{12}$ denotes a very short-range force, while a dependence on $1/r^2$ denotes a long-range force. The bands of forces are summarized in Table 1.

TABLE 1

Force	Type of force	Variation with distance
Gravitational or electrostatic	Weak and long range	$\dfrac{1}{r^2}$
Inter-molecular attractive forces	Weak, rather short range	$\dfrac{1}{r^7}$
Intra-molecular attractive forces (chemical bonds)	Strong, very short range	$\dfrac{1}{r^{10}}$
Forces within the nucleus	Extremely strong but of extremely short range	$\dfrac{1}{r^{15}}$

This natural non-random distribution of forces into bands *must* result in our finding a relatively simple behaviour of matter, and certainly no simple behaviour could be expected if there were a rather smooth, continuous distribution of forces. The existence of discrete bands in the force spectrum (Fig. 5.4) is reflected in the wide acceptance that in many diverse phenomena the "billiard ball" atomic theory "works" quite well. The reason that the theory of the atom as a scaled-down billiard ball does work so well is that within each molecule the atoms remain sharply distinguished, while the (larger) molecules (e.g. of sugar) also remain quite sharply distinguished, in their turn, from each other and from any solvent in which they may be dissolved. This simple behaviour, a result of the intra- and inter-molecular forces being of different strengths and ranges, is also responsible for the constancy of the Avogadro number N referred to above. The "billiard ball" model is thus a good theoretical model of a molecule, and recent work with the electron-microscope has made it possible to photograph single molecules, giving results consistent with this simple model (Figs. 5.5 through 5.9). Another simple finding, following extensive measurements, has been the constancy of the resting mass of the electron and proton. Again, extremely powerful forces, very short range in action, must be responsible. The consistency of these various theoretical models, over a wide

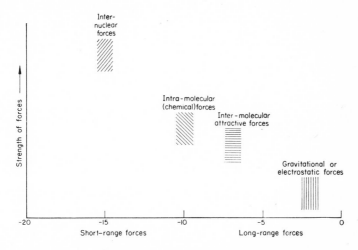

FIG. 5.4. Schematic representation of the bands of naturally occurring attractive forces. Here the strength of the force is plotted against the corresponding power variation of r (where r is the distance of separation between the bodies concerned). For example, for gravity, the force is weak and varies as the inverse square of the distance of separation of the two masses (i.e. the power is -2). Note that the forces are not shown to scale, and that in practice the bands may be wider than shown here, leading to slight interference with one another, and causing many of the simple "laws" to be of only moderate accuracy.

range of physical experiments, endows the particles with what is often called "reality".

That the forces within the atomic nucleus are so powerful and of such short range explains the usual finding that the rate of radioactive decay (y) is independent of all other factors, i.e. it obeys the equation $y = A$. Occasionally, however, there may be evidence of slight "overlap" with the next band of forces (i.e. intra-molecular chemical bonds), leading to slight deviations from the simple law: this occurs with beryllium-7, whose rate of radioactive decay changes by about $0 \cdot 1\%$

when its atoms are incorporated into certain chemical compounds. Thus, if x refers to chemical bonding, $y = A + B\Delta x$, though B is admittedly small.

The success of the "scaling-down" analogy in theorizing may now be seen to lie in the rather wide separations of the force bands. Thus, compared with gravitation, inter-molecular forces are different in range

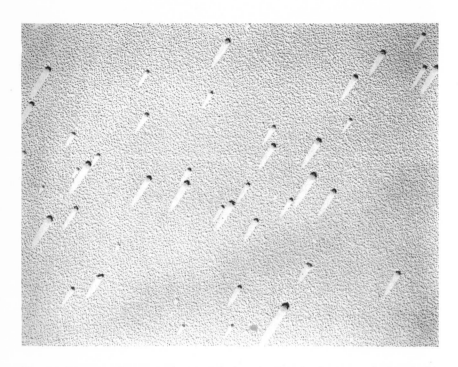

FIG. 5.5. Electron-microscope picture of single molecules of polystyrene, shadowed with platinum. The single molecules (i.e. the small shadowed spheres) are about 0·1 cm diameter, and so, since the magnification in this print is 70,000 times, the volume of a single molecule is about $1 \cdot 7 \times 10^{-18}$ cm^3, corresponding to a molecular weight of about 1·2 million. This photograph was taken by Dr. M. J. Richardson, and is reproduced with his permission. (See also *Proc. roy. Soc.* **A279**, 50 (1964).)

by a factor of r^5, and so weak is the gravitational field relative to the inter-molecular forces that a normal billiard ball remains very closely spherical in practice. If we now scale this system down, we see that compared with inter-molecular forces, *intra*-molecular forces are different in range by a factor of r^3, so that the success of the simple billiard-ball model of an atom is explicable. Scaling-down through

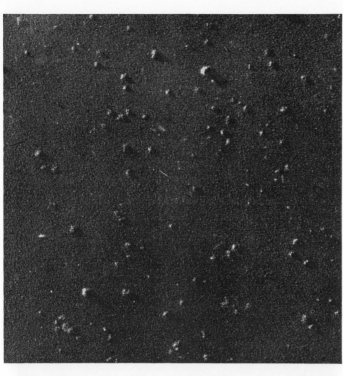

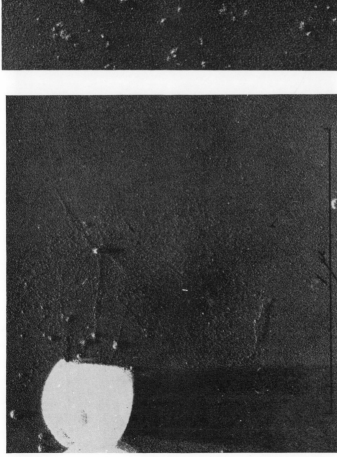

FIG. 5.6. (a) Thread-like molecule of hydroxyethylcellulose of molecular weight 125,000. The thread at the bottom seems to be arched like a bow over the support. The large white particle is a sphere of polystyrene latex. Magnification is 75,000 times. (b) Single molecules (and clumps of several molecules) of hydroxyethylcellulose, collapsed into spheres. Most of these spheres contain only one molecule. The magnification is 100,000 times. These pictures were taken with an electron microscope by Dr. Nils Gellerstedt, and are reproduced with permission. (See also *Arkiv Kemi.* **20**, (11), 147, 1962.)

another band, we see that since the nuclear forces are of shorter range than the intra-molecular forces by a factor of about r^5, the consistency with experiment of the billiard-ball model of the nucleus is explicable.

FIG. 5.7. Tungsten crystal of approximately 400×10^{-8} cm radius. The magnification of this enlargement is about one million times. Individual atoms of tungsten are visible (particularly in the 111 planes as arrowed) in this photograph, taken by Dr. Erwin W. Müller using his "field-ion" microscope. See also his paper "Field Ion Microscopy of Surface Structures on an Atomic Scale", American Society for Testing Materials (1962).

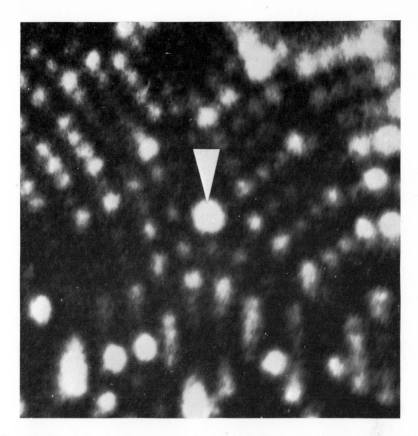

FIG. 5.8. Nitrogen molecule (arrowed) adsorbed at 78°K on to an iridium surface. The magnification here is about 10,000,000 times. This, and Fig. 5.9, are reproduced by kind permission of Dr. J. F. Mulson and Dr. E. W. Müller (see also *J. Chem. Phys.*, **38**, 2615, 1963).

Inside the nucleus there are further particles, the nucleons, which are like even smaller billiard balls.

A strong tendency to symmetry in nature is another result of the "band" distribution of attractive forces. There is a general tendency to contraction within each band, and consequently gravitation keeps the stars roughly spherical, liquids are pulled by inter-molecular forces into spherical drops, and matter is concentrated into apparently symmetrical atomic nuclei. The elegant simplicity of nature and of many scientific theories, noted by Poincaré and quoted in Chapter 1, thus stems from the "band" distribution of forces in nature.

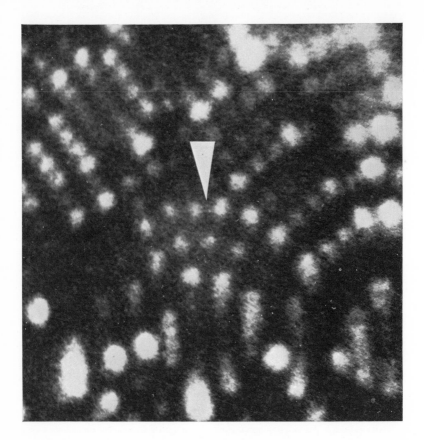

FIG. 5.9. Iridium surface from which the nitrogen molecule has been desorbed, showing that the adsorption site was over two adjacent atoms of iridium. (Compare Figure 5.8.)

To summarize, we find that there are many simple correlations in science. After allowing for the subjective element in that we often *choose* to work theoretically, at least in pure science, with the most tractable systems (i.e. the simplest systems), we find that there still remains an impressive proportion of rather simple general "laws". The latter are of considerable accuracy, indicating that the terms such as f'' and higher derivatives in eq. (iv) are small. Physically, we can understand this through the finding that forces in nature are grouped

Fig. 5.10. Symmetry in nature as shown by snowflakes. From W. A. Bentley and W. J. Humphries, "Snow Crystals", McGraw-Hill, N.Y. (1931). (Reproduced with permission.)

in quite distinct and well-separated bands of range and strength, so that there is little overlap between them; consequently it is often satisfactory (to a first approximation) to scale-up or scale-down some quite simple theoretical model.

Chapter 6
Prediction and Probability

PREDICTIONS

In order to predict what is expected to happen in the future, one can extend a graph of what is happening now. This process of extension is known as extrapolation. Of course one can always extrapolate the graph of *any* straight line, or even of a smooth curved line, to predict what might happen in the future, or what apparently happened in the past; but how much reliance do we feel we can place on the extrapolated part of the graph?

One may equally well extrapolate a correlation not involving time, for example Hooke's law for the stretching of a spring (Fig. 6.1). This latter example shows clearly the possible errors of extrapolation; as heavier weights are loaded on to a spring it extends proportionately only up to a certain limit, beyond which it breaks. Extrapolation into this region would thus have involved us in serious error.

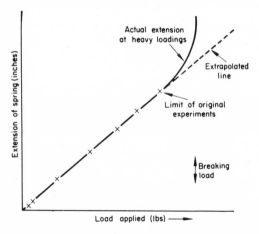

FIG. 6.1. Hooke's law for the stretching of a spring: the extension (above its length unloaded) is directly proportional to the load applied. The extrapolated region (broken line) is unreliable, as the spring will break under a certain critical applied load.

68

To assist in extrapolating experimental results a straight-line plot or some other smooth, quite simple curve is desirable. Thus while we may with some slight confidence extrapolate the straight line plot on p. 58 simply by extending the straight line either to the right or to the left, a less simple graph (e.g. the curve on p. 59) is much less easy to extrapolate with any confidence. The meaning of simplicity in a straight-line relationship has already been discussed. Whether it involves an apparently more complex or less sophisticated mathematical form is unimportant here; the number of arbitrary constants is the factor that determines simplicity.

In extrapolating a straight-line plot, one intuitively assumes a rule analogous to Newton's "First Law of Motion". This states that a body moving uniformly along a straight-line path will continue to do so unless or until some force begins to act on that body. The application of this rule to the extrapolation of a straight-line plot is that "the correlation will continue as a straight-line plot unless or until some new factor becomes significant", or, in other words, the course of the plot (or of the system) will not change unless something changes it. In this latter form the rule seems almost trivial; but in practice it is often difficult to find which factors may have been absent or relatively unimportant in the well-studied part of the plot, but which are calculated to become important in the region of extrapolation. For example, if a car accelerates smoothly from rest up to 30 m.p.h. in a period of 10 seconds, we could extrapolate either the plots of velocity versus distance or velocity versus time; and if we plotted the latter (Fig. 6.2), we could predict that after 60 seconds the car would be travelling at 180 m.p.h. Experiment would show, of course, that this prediction was in very serious error: various retarding factors such as

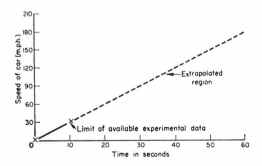

FIG. 6.2. This figure illustrates the absurdity of extrapolating a line without trying to allow for new factors which may operate. At higher speeds the air resistance will prevent the speed of the car increasing beyond a certain limit.

air resistance become increasingly important as the higher speeds are reached.

It may be noted from this example that it does not matter whether the extrapolation is one in space or in time; the same arguments apply to both. For example, the stretching spring will obey Hooke's straight-line relationship (the extension being directly proportional to the load applied) until an extension is reached at which the metal is seriously weakened and starts to crack and break. Equally well we might have extrapolated against time the relationship that "the extension of the spring is always the same for a given load and independent of time", as in Fig. 6.3. But such extrapolation to long times is always dangerous;

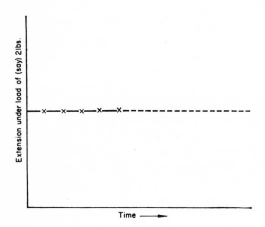

FIG. 6.3. Finding that the extension of the spring or fibre is the same after several measurements does not mean that it is safe to extrapolate; fatigue may set in.

after a sufficient time, during which we may have applied and removed the load many times, the metal of the spring will become fatigued, and the spring will break. This sudden onset of metal fatigue is well known to be of particular importance in the aircraft industry. Even if we do not repeatedly load and unload the spring, the material may oxidize or show "creep" over a period of time. It is well known that glass fibres under load appear stable for some time, and then suddenly break. It is thus clear that further experiments or observations are always desirable, the more so the longer the extrapolation and the less we know of the fundamentals of the system. Another example of the possible errors of extrapolation is furnished by plotting the birth-rate in Great Britain (Fig. 6.4). Extrapolation from period up to 1932 to the year 1967 would

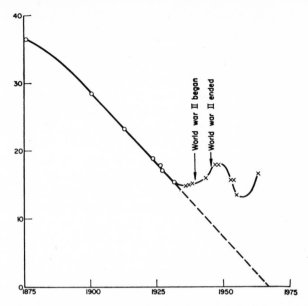

Fig. 6.4. Births per year per 1000 population ("crude" birth-rate) for England and Wales. Circles refer to data up to 1932; the heavy line drawn through these points is rectilinear since 1900. Extrapolation of the decreasing birth-rate (broken line) beyond 1932 clearly gives predictions which have proved quite wrong in practice (actual figures being shown by crosses), due to the influence of new social factors. (Data taken from *Encyclopædia Britannica*.)

have predicted a birth-rate of zero! Clearly new social factors (war, prosperity, housing) have become operative since 1932, so that alarmist extrapolations from earlier decades (common during the 1930's) were not, in practice, either well founded or accurate.

In general, we should extrapolate a plot only when there is no known reason why we should not do so, but here ignorance can be very dangerous, and we must search for any factor likely to alter the extrapolation. One might perhaps argue that extrapolation would be completely reliable if one knew all the factors which could possibly alter the course of the events under study, but the significant word in this argument is *if*. In practice, there can never be certainty that all possible variables have been taken into account.

THE ROLE OF THEORY IN PREDICTION

The role of theory in extrapolation is that, by allowing for certain factors which operate, it enables us to extrapolate a little more confidently. For example let us assume that we have a theory with which the known experiments or observations are consistent, and in which we believe we have included every relevant factor. If this theory indicates that the relationship would still hold outside the present range of measurements, it is with increased confidence that we then extrapolate into the untested region. The more comprehensive the theory in including various possible factors and forces, the more confidence we have in using it in the extrapolation. In betting terms, we prefer to place our money on something about which we have as much inside information as possible. But even so, we can never be sure that we have allowed for every factor which might operate significantly in the extrapolated range. We cannot apply mathematical probability theory with any more justification than we can to horse racing. Moreover, if our theory is admittedly not very comprehensive, and we feel uneasily that we may well not have included all the possible variables, we necessarily place less trust in the extrapolation. At the extreme end of the confidence scale is an extrapolation such as that of a straight line through three experimental points, extended in either direction. Here, without a detailed theory or knowledge of the system, we have theorized simply and rather negatively that since no obvious reason has occurred to us, why the relationship should not remain linear, we shall extrapolate the line. Clearly such extrapolated values would correspond to the outsider in a race ; optimism replaces confidence.

In making long-range forecasts of the weather one again extrapolates ; one method uses the theory that the future weather will develop along the same lines as it did in other years when the present and immediate past weather patterns were very similar to those of this year. An important question here is the precision with which forecasts are made. They can, like some astrological forecasts, be so vague as to be irrefutable, or they can specify within close limits what temperatures, rainfall, etc. are expected. The latter forecasts are, of course, readily refutable, and indeed are often refuted ; but until better theories of weather forecasting are available, even an admittedly rather unreliable prediction can be acted upon rather more confidently than can an uninformed guess.

A second long-range forecast involves engineering design and materials of construction. Figure 6.5 shows how the weight of various engines (of a given power) has been progressively reduced by better design and the development of lighter materials. It is seen that the curves are all rather similar in form, and Mr. H. Constant, who published this graph in 1954, extrapolated them from that time as shown by the broken lines.

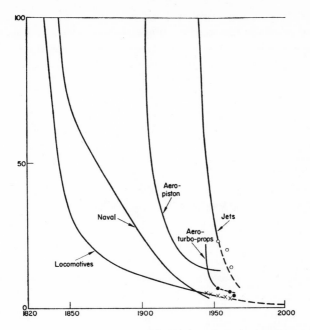

FIG. 6.5. Relative improvement with time of weights of various engines of a given power output (H. Constant (1954); figure reproduced with permission). The curves form a family with remarkable similarities, suggesting that engines of widely differing types are lightened to very much the same extent by development. But each new development seems to occur more rapidly than earlier developments, so that developments of recent engines (such as jets) may well be nearly complete as soon as those begun a century earlier, if the extrapolations (made in 1954 by H. Constant, and indicated by broken lines) are valid. Crosses and circles indicate recent figures (inserted by the present writer), to be compared with the extrapolations.

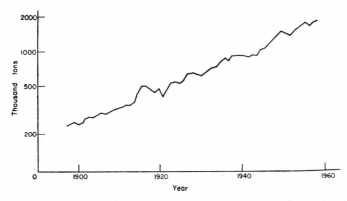

FIG. 6.6. Consumption of alkali (on logarithmic scale) in the U.K. and Eire, 1897–1959, from data of Mumford.

Another interesting application of extrapolation in long-range forecasting concerns the market demand for a product. Sometimes the plot is surprisingly simple, particularly when the product (e.g. alkali, as in Fig. 6.6) is used in many diverse industries. Changes in the exact

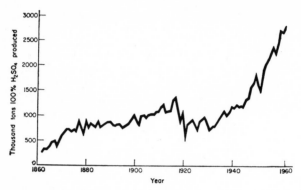

FIG. 6.7. Production of sulphuric acid in the U.K. as a function of time (after Mumford).

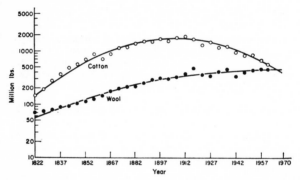

FIG. 6.8. Consumption (on logarithmic scale) of cotton in the U.K. as a function of time. The line drawn through the points is a parabola. How far can it be extrapolated? The same graph shows that the consumption of wool is still increasing (after Mumford).

pattern of usage over the years in the different industries are evidently irrelevant, and one may extrapolate with fair confidence. For sulphuric acid, however, the demand curve (Fig. 6.7) is much less smooth, and one extrapolates with less confidence, for many complex factors are evidently operative. Simple curves are often found for consumer products, particularly cotton, wool and man-made fibres (Figs. 6.8 and 6.9). Before extrapolating, one naturally tries to take all the relevant factors into account, including those which are not yet significant but which one believes may become so. For example, one must bear in mind the

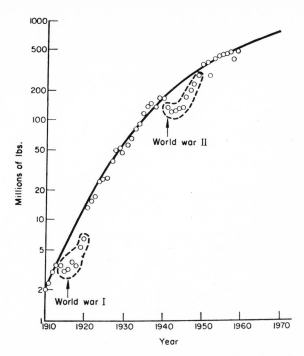

Fɪɢ. 6.9. U.K. production of man-made fibres (on logarithmic scale) as function of time (after Mumford). If one rejects the production figures during World War I and World War II (thus treating these fibres as luxury articles), the fitted curve obeys the Gompertz equation: log (production) $= k - ab^{-t}$. This suggests that if the curve is extrapolated to a very great time t, the market is then saturated at a limit given by log (production) $= k$. Here k, a and b are arbitrary constants.

possibilities that there may perhaps be a change from using sulphuric acid to using nitric acid in the extraction of phosphate rock for fertilizer, or that perhaps other industries at present using little sulphuric acid are coming to a period of rapid growth. The skill of the forecaster lies in taking as many potential variables as possible into consideration.

Forecasting electricity demand is of particular importance, since the time interval between forecasting the need for a new power station and bringing it into service is over five years. It has often been assumed that the peak demand d for electricity will increase exponentially with time t according to the quite simple (two arbitrary constants) equation:

$$d = a\, e^{bt} \qquad \text{(viii)}$$

In logarithmic form, this becomes:

$$\log d = \log a + bt \qquad \text{(ix)}$$

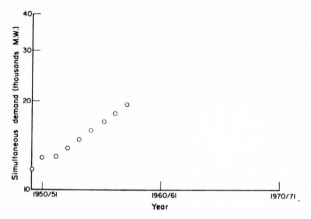

Fig. 6.10. Maximum simultaneous demand for electricity in England and Wales in winters 1949/50 to 1957/58, from data of Edwards and Clark. The demand figures (in thousands of megawatts) are plotted on a logarithmic scale in this and subsequent figures.

which implies a straight-line relation between log d and t. Figure 6.10, in which d is plotted on a logarithmic scale, illustrates how log d increased in England and Wales from 1949/50 to 1957/58. With what confidence can we draw a straight line through these points and extrapolate it to the years ahead? To answer this, one must decide (i)

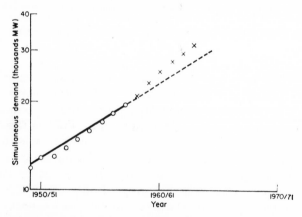

Fig. 6.11. Through the points of Fig. 6.10 a straight line (drawn heavily) has been passed, and extrapolated from 1957/58 to 1964/65. The extrapolated forecast figures (published by the electricity industry in 1958) are quoted in the report from the Select Committee. The straight line has a slope corresponding to an annual increase of 6%. Actual maximum simultaneous demand is represented on the figure by crosses. The industry's forecast figure for 1962/63 was 26,400 megawatts, but actual demand was 29,600 MW.

whether it seems at all reasonable to draw any straight line through the points, and (ii) if so, what is the slope of the line with the best fit.

If one tries to put a straight line through the data of Fig. 6.10 (circles), one can obtain the heavy line of Fig. 6.11, which is of the form of equation (ix); on its extrapolation (broken line) were based the official forecasts of the future expansion of the industry (Report from the Select Committee, p. 35).

It is seen just how serious the error of using this particular extrapolation was by the gap (on a logarithmic scale, it must be remembered) between the actual demand and the extrapolated curve in Fig. 6.11.

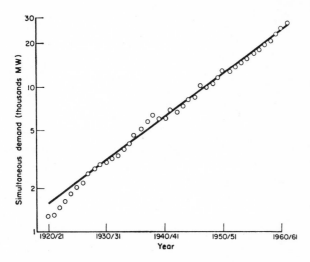

FIG. 6.12. The long-term annual increase in the simultaneous maximum demand for electricity in England and Wales has been 7%. (Data from Edwards and Clark.)

This discrepancy arose from two sources:

(a) if the line to be put through the points must be straight, the full line of Fig. 6.11 has too low a slope. (The reader can himself try putting a ruler through the points of Figs. 6.10 or 6.11.) The line of Fig. 6.11 has a slope corresponding to an annual increase in peak demand of only 6%, though the long-term growth (Fig. 6.12) indicates an annual growth of 7%. Had a line of the latter slope been drawn through the points of Fig. 6.10, the prediction would have been better although still too low, as shown in Fig. 6.13.

(b) the forecast would have been better had a curve represented by the equation

$$d = a \log [1 + b \, e^{ct}] \qquad (x)$$

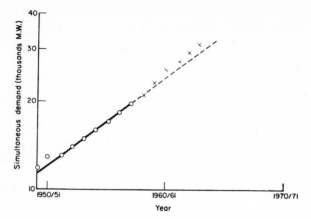

FIG. 6.13. Through the points of Fig. 6.10 the present writer has drawn a straight line representing a 7% annual increase. This slope is that shown by the long-term trend in Fig. 6.12. The discrepancy in the 60's is clearly less than that in Fig. 6.11, but is still serious. Forecast demand in 1962/63 would have been 28,000 MW, whereas actual demand was 29,600 MW.

been used instead of eq. (viii). This equation contains three arbitrary constants, and in Fig. 6.14 it is seen that the extrapolation based on it fits the recent demand figures (again plotted on a logarithmic scale) remarkably well.

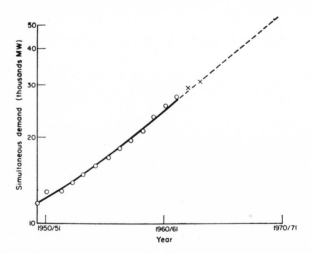

FIG. 6.14. Curve of eq. (x) has been drawn through the points of actual demand (circles, again on a logarithmic scale) and used for extrapolation. This curve was suggested by Edwards and Clark, but they did not favour using it on the grounds that there appeared to be no convincing reason for preferring it to the straight-line plot of eq. (ix). Crosses refer to recent actual demand.

Investigating why the projected demand of Fig. 6.11, on which the expansion plans of the electricity supply industry were based, was in such serious error, the Select Committee stated that for the extrapolation "the choice of the exponential curve is a complex mathematical exercise". Of course this justification of eq. (ix) is simply not true—the choice is an act of faith, a faith which might have been held with slightly more confidence because of the form of the long-term demand (Fig. 6.12), provided that the planned annual increase had been taken to be 7% and that no new factors had been significant. But an annual increase of only 6% was allowed for, and, further, a significant new factor (a rise in the use of domestic space heaters) was becoming important, to allow for which an extra arbitrary constant in the demand equation (i.e. replacing eq. (ix) by eq. (x)) is evidently required. Indeed, the investigation of the Select Committee found that between 1955 and 1961 there had been no major survey of domestic demand; this was regarded as a major omission.

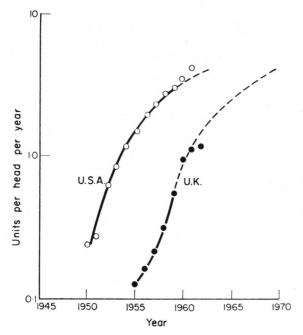

FIG. 6.15. Number of aerosol units (on logarithmic scale) manufactured per year in the U.K. and the U.S. per head of population. The broken portions of the curves are extrapolations, with which figures for subsequent years are in quite good agreement. Are the trends in the U.K. and the U.S. no longer quite parallel because British people are more resistant to applying shaving cream, toothpaste, etc. from aerosol containers? (Data from Mumford.)

Analogy is often helpful in extrapolation. Electricity demand in the U.K. can be more confidently expected to increase for many years by analogy with the U.S., where, though the electricity consumption per head is already very much greater than in the U.K., the straight-line semi-log plot (eq. (ix)) shows no tendency to flatten off. Another example of the use of analogy is in the use of pressurized dispensers (Fig. 6.15), where the tendency to flattening in the U.S. curve is used to extrapolate the U.K. curve, with what accuracy we shall be able to judge in the next few years.

PROBABILITY THEORY

The extrapolation of probability theory provides an interesting example of the unreliability and error that can arise. As an example, consider the curve of normal error given by the expression

$$y = A\, e^{-b(x-x_1)^2} \tag{xi}$$

This represents the curve shown in Fig. 6.16 where y approaches closely towards zero when x is very large or very small, but never quite reaches zero.

To this quite simple mathematical expression of probability many observations can be fitted, at least in the region around the peak of the

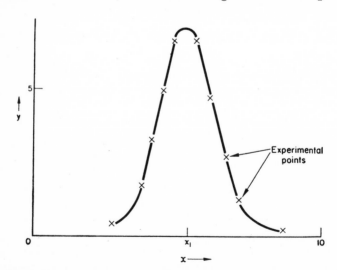

FIG. 6.16. Curve of normal error, eq. (xi). Experimental points are in close accord with this curve in the region around the peak, but the theoretical curve never quite reaches zero.

curve (Fig. 6.16): y could be the number of craters on the moon of depth x in a given area. While, however, the plot of eq. (xi) might fit the data around the peak of the curve, we know that there are, in any area we select, certainly no craters as deep as (say) 10,000 miles. Thus while probability functions of the type of eq. (xi) are useful in covering the data near $x = x_1$, the function cuts off in practice; when $(x - x_1)$ is very large, y can become zero, though of course this is impossible according to the simple eq. (xi). Extrapolation of eq. (xi) to large values of $(x - x_1)$ may thus lead to absurd results.

Another example arises in the toxicity of reagents to living cells, or in haemolysis. In the latter, for example, y represents the number of cells of a resistance x to haemolysis, being measured by the amount of haemolytic agent required. Such a distribution of resistances in a population is quite general, but members never have resistances greater or less than certain values, though the fit around the peak of the curve may be excellent.

These two examples show that extrapolation to very large values can involve absurdities if the extrapolated points are interpreted physically. The probability function (xi) must therefore be slightly incorrect as a representation of what is happening in practice because of neglect of certain factors. Extrapolation to large or small values of x, when y is very small, results in these factors being significant relative to the small values of y. One can therefore modify eq. (xi) to take account of this. For example one may write

$$y = A\,e^{-b(x-x_1)^2} - c \qquad\qquad \text{(xii)}$$

where c is small and positive. The probability thus falls to zero at very high or low values of x. Only when the term c is known, from a detailed study of the system, can eq. (xii) be used accurately at high and low values of x. Around the peak, however, where measurements are generally made, the term c and the factors responsible for it will generally be relatively unimportant, and too small to determine experimentally.

Summarizing, we see that though extrapolation is widely used, it has no logical basis, nor can we calculate the probability of an extrapolated curve being accurate. Unless the extrapolation of a relatively simple curve leads to obvious absurdities, we may extrapolate it ignoring any small irregularities. Theory plays a leading role in that if we know something about the variables which are operative, we can better decide how much confidence to place in the prediction. It is always necessary to continue further tests and observations to check the extrapolation.

Chapter 7
Science and Society

SCIENCE AND OUR CIVILIZATION

At the present time we in the Western world are spending rapidly increasing sums of money on training increasing numbers of scientists. How should these best be employed in society? Of course, one obvious place is in the laboratory, where they may produce new gadgets like transistor radios, new plastics like polypropylene, or supersonic jet airliners. Such items, it is true, may perhaps be regarded as luxury toys for the jaded appetites of the Western world, but a much stronger reason for having a body of trained experts is that they engender a sense of confidence that any difficulties which might arise over the supply of really important items could be rapidly overcome.

Consider, as an example, how readily we now assume that food production can be carried on indefinitely, that we can always replace easily the phosphates and nitrates removed from the soil, which can consequently be used over and over again without depletion. Indeed, we are confident that if the soil did become exhausted of some hitherto undefined essential component, chemical engineers would be able to produce millions of sacks full of this substance for the farmers to spread on the land.

This freedom from soil depletion has never been achieved in past civilizations; shortages of wood for fuel, and of food, have been advanced as causes of the decline of the Roman Empire. Indeed, one may make an arguable case that the great civilizations of the past have, one by one, decayed simply because food supplies became increasingly meagre in consequence of a decline in agricultural productivity.

This applies to the earliest food cultivators, the growers of wheat and barley in the hills of western Asia, in the seventh millennium B.C. It applies also to the early river-valley civilizations of north-west India and Mesopotamia, to Persia, and to the Roman Empire; the increasing population of Italy at the time of the Punic Wars soon led to overcultivation of the Apennine Peninsula. The Romans, having no scientists, sought a military solution to this problem, and the territory of Carthage became the chief granary of the Romans in the succeeding centuries. This, according to Professor F. E. Zeuner, was why so much importance was attached to the province of Africa, and why, when the Vandals invaded that continent in the fifth century, they struck literally at the roots of Rome's existence. The Vandals were not entirely responsible, however; the Romans themselves exploited the steppe land of northern Africa, and by their efforts so denuded the land that what were fields are now desert, and Roman wells, cisterns and even olive-oil factories (evidence that the soil once bore olive groves) stand today among the shifting sands of North Africa.

Fig. 7.1. Ruin of Roman olive-oil factory in North Africa (photograph by the author).

If diminishing food or fuel supplies have been an important cause of the long-term decay of civilizations, then ours has a better chance of surviving, partly because our soil is denuded more slowly in our moister climates, but largely because of our large-scale production of nitrate and phosphate fertilizers, and of nuclear fuels. The new phenomenon of large-scale production made possible by scientists has, of course, its concomitant disadvantages, one of the most obvious being the 50-megaton hydrogen bomb. But we may debate whether the continuous fear of nuclear war is not less demoralizing than the fears of past ages, fears of war and disease and hunger. Though our civilization

8*

has not eliminated war, gone are the days of the sacking of our cities by warriors armed with bows and poisoned arrows or with bayonets, and Western society is now free from fears of many diseases, including tuberculosis. We have also virtually eliminated malnutrition and famine in countries which practise the large-scale production and use of pest-control chemicals and of nitrate and phosphate. Considering all these points, I do not wish that I had been born (as a member of the proletariat!) in an earlier age.

An oft-repeated criticism of the study of any physical science is that it distracts attention from spirituality, that it produces only highly specialized practitioners rather than fully educated men. Why can we not return, is the cry, to the fully educated man of Newton's day?

It is by no means clear that this problem of specialization is confined to science graduates. It is not obvious that the Ph.D. graduate who has specialized in, say, the works of some medieval French writer is any less restricted or more fully educated than a Ph.D. graduate in a science department. Indeed, the problem in education today is one of narrow-mindedness rather than specialization. Just as all science undergraduates should have the time and stimulation to find out something about music, literature and art, so the man reading liberal arts should come to know something about science. Of course he cannot be expected to know very much about the factual side, but he *should* know something about science as a philosophical movement, its aims and methods, and how aesthetically satisfying can be the unification of concepts achieved in a scientific theory. Indeed, one can argue a case that while poetry has lost much of its popular appeal, that while there appears no new literary romance comparable to Héloise and Abelard, the great romance of the twentieth century is (as one of Lawrence Durrell's characters phrased it) the marriage of space and time in relativity theory. The boldness and imaginative sweep of many scientific hypotheses, the necessity of checking them by experiment, and the importance of criticism (even of established authority) are what should be taught to *all* university students.

The solution to the problem of students having insufficient time to study broadly cannot be met by *less* specialization, however. Since we in Britain and the United States do not really want to lower our living standards to those of past centuries, nor even to return to the drab days of unemployment and political discontent in the 1930's, our scientists *must* be highly specialized to take their place in a highly competitive world. The solution to the problem of specialization, then, in so far as it is a problem, must be to specialize even further, so that the student, whether in arts or science, will train to have a highly specialized knowledge in a very small field. Only then will he have time to develop his general knowledge over a much wider field. This is one way in which we can avoid the dangers of Lord Snow's "two cultures" in which he pictures the arts graduate administrator in his front office and the science graduate in his back laboratory, with too little in common to make possible effective communication between them.

Another way of dealing with the danger of the gap in common understanding and communication is already making itself manifest. It is the aptitude, ability and enthusiasm of many scientists for tackling some of the problems concerning people, society, the way various devices should best be used, and economics. If scientists are successful in these operations, if they gain the confidence of the people that they can run such things as railways or operations of war as efficiently as they run chemical plants and instrument companies, then the "two-cultures" stratification of society should soon trouble us no more. If this indeed comes about in Britain, the so-called "brain drain" should become less serious, since our scientists will then have the financial reward, the status and the facilities (I deliberately put them in this order) which will generally make it worth while to remain in Britain. It would be a tragedy if the acceptance of the scientist in Britain comes about so slowly (compared with his acceptance in the U.S.) that the present very serious loss of some of our most enquiring minds and best university teachers continues unabated.

The problems of our society in Britain are serious ; exports, education, economics and transportation are among the most pressing. We need new and better products to capture export markets, particularly in Europe and the U.S.; we need to solve the problems of transportation in our congested cities and on our narrow roads, we need to be able to attract (and hold) first class minds to educate our brightest youth and we want economic stability. Can scientists assist in the formulation and solution of these problems ? Indeed they can. Besides inventing new gadgets and materials, scientists have already, since the early days of World War II, played an increasingly important role in solving the problems of our society, where there are usually many variables but often a paucity of numerical data. The scientist, with his enquiring mind, with his talent and enthusiasm for thinking up a general theory which incorporates the important variables, has proved to be a most suitably trained person to undertake such studies. Similarly, his special knowledge of how to set up mathematical equations derived from theory is absolutely necessary if deductions from theories are to be sufficiently quantitative for numerical predictions to be made. Such studies are known as operational research.

7

OPERATIONAL RESEARCH

Operational research is the application of the methods of the research scientist to various rather complex practical operations, such as those of production, of war, of economics and of social affairs. For example, it has often been suggested that relatively too much effort is expended in the production of new devices, with relatively too little effort in using the existing devices to best advantage. For such problems as predicting quantitatively how best existing devices could be used, operational research is particularly useful. A paucity of numerical data with which to work is a usual characteristic of the operations to which operational research is applied. Sometimes operational research can also be used to find whether and when a change-over to a new device would be worth while.

The first role of the scientist is to formulate a theory about what factors are important in controlling the result of a particular operation. He must then deduce from this theory the relative importance, in quantitative terms, of each factor in turn, even though in practice they all act together. Sometimes *experiments* are possible, but often (as with economic systems) only *observations* can be made, with several important factors acting simultaneously. Fortunately it often happens in practice that individual factors are relatively stable over quite long periods of time.

In formal terms, if R is the result of the operation, and if the hypothesis is that factors x_1, x_2, x_3, etc. are important, then one can write

$$R = f(x_1, x_2, x_3 \ldots x_n) \tag{xiii}$$

For any small change ΔR in the result, one may write

$$\Delta R = \frac{\partial R}{\partial x_1} \Delta x_1 + \frac{\partial R}{\partial x_2} \Delta x_2 + \text{etc.} \tag{xiv}$$

where $\partial R/\partial x_1$ etc. are the factors which are, according to the theory, constant and independent provided that the change is small. The partial derivative operator (∂) implies that all the other factors x are kept constant while one particular x is varied.

It was during World War II that operational research developed particularly rapidly. One study, typical of many, arose in 1942 over the best use of the limited constructional resources in getting supplies across the Atlantic, i.e. of countering most effectively the German submarine attacks. In particular, the problem was one of deciding whether to build more merchant vessels or more escort vessels, and

FIG. 7.2. Air cover greatly reduced losses of ships. (Reproduced with the permission of the Imperial War Museum.)

whether to use the available planes for bombing Germany or for protecting the Atlantic shipping.

In his book "Studies of War", Professor P. M. S. Blackett gives an exciting first-hand account of this and other investigations. The first step in tackling the shipping problem was to theorize that the shipping losses were a function of four principal variables: size of convoy, speed of convoy, number of armed escort vessels, and amount of air cover.

Comparison of this theory, in the form of eqs. (xiii) and (xiv), with the losses suffered in the Atlantic during the previous two years led to the following conclusions. Each additional escort vessel put into service could be expected to save between two and three merchant ships per year. Provided, therefore, that the war was expected to go on for a further year or more, it should pay to build more escort vessels at the expense of building fewer merchant ships. This result, however, was not particularly useful because of the practical difficulties of changing the shipyards over from building merchant vessels to building escort vessels. Another conclusion was that, other things being equal, a relatively fast convoy, with a speed of nine knots, should suffer only about half the losses of a slow convoy of speed seven knots, provided that air cover was available to both. Further, if air cover could be provided for as long as eight hours a day, the losses of ships should be decreased by one-third. The size of the convoy was also a very important factor, according to the analysis, which indicated that increasing the number of ships per convoy from 32 to 57 should reduce losses by 56%.

The very high values of the speed and the air cover factors, which came as rather a surprise, enabled a rough estimate to be made of the profitability of the various possible changes.

As a second example of operational research, let us consider what determines the rate of flow of traffic on a rural two-lane road. Here Dr. A. J. Miller, of the Department of Transportation of Birmingham University, has propounded a theory of the possible factors affecting the flow of traffic on a two-lane road. The overtaking rate, which is the important variable, might be affected by the quantity of approaching traffic, by hills, by bends, by weather, by the composition of the traffic, by the time of day, etc. The quantitative expression of these factors (rather as in eqs. (xiii) and (xiv)) is then written down and compared with detailed observations to find which factors are particularly important in causing delays to the traffic. Following this sort of analysis, one should be able to deduce whether one could most profitably spend the limited

Fig. 7.3. Bunches of traffic on rural two-lane road in bad weather. (Photograph by Aerofilms and Aero Pictorial, Ltd.)

funds allocated for road improvement on constructing a third lane, or whether it would be better to eliminate the bends and steep hills on the two-lane road.

HISTORICAL THEORIES

An historical "law" is usually put forward in the very simple form

$$R = f(x) \qquad\qquad (xv)$$

where R is the course of history (which is so often claimed to run in cycles). Here R is manifested by the behaviour of a group of people, and x is one single variant. For example, x might be economic forces, or it might be the availability of land, or the availability of food, or the climate, or the popular enthusiasms of the people or the strength of character of the leader. Even in physics such simple functions determined by only one variable are rare, so it is perhaps not surprising that when data are advanced to support any one of these particular theoretical interpretations, adherents of rival theories assert that the data used have been carefully *selected* to be in accord with the theory concerned, and hence the "support" for the theory. This difficulty arises in part from the erroneous belief that it is possible to "prove" one's law or theory. We have seen in previous chapters that a general theory can *never* be proved, but rather should one continue to test its predictions more precisely and over ever wider ranges of experience. Then the theory may conceivably be refuted.

An example of an historical theory which made erroneous predictions is provided by Marxism in its original form. This theory predicted that the socialist revolution would be an *industrial* transformation, involving the overthrow of developed capitalism by the workers, because of the following argument. Capitalism must lead to increases in wealth for the few and of misery for the working class; it can, therefore, only be destroyed, not reformed. But as Popper (1945, 1962) has pointed out, this prediction has not been borne out by the revolution of 1917 in Russia (which was then very backward industrially), nor by the growth of limited socialism (democratic governmental interference with laissez-faire economics) in such countries as Sweden and New Zealand.

Thus, by subsequent testing of theoretical predictions certain historical theories can be refuted, particularly those of the simple form of eq. (xv). In this way all these very simple historical theories prove inadequate.

But, one may argue, supposing that one evolved a more complete theory, of the form :

$$R = f(x_1, x_2, x_3 \ldots x_n) \qquad \text{(xiii)}$$

where x_1, x_2, etc. refer to the variables listed above. Could this not be satisfactory? The difficulty here is that this relationship is now more complex, therefore, it is very difficult to test; nevertheless, there can be some progress within the field of historical interpretation. Some theories are demonstrably false and can be eliminated, some can be abandoned because they are less simple or less general than others which "work" equally well, and they can all (in principle) be tested against the available data by the technique of eq. (xiv).

The controversy over the causes of the outbreak of World War II provides an interesting example of the difficulty of explaining the course of history in precise, testable terms. The historian A. J. P. Taylor has formulated the theory that "the war of 1939, far from being premeditated, was a mistake: the result, on both sides, of diplomatic blunders", and that "Hitler's practical plans for war were very second rate...incompetent and casual". Further, "Hitler did not make plans for world-conquest or for anything else"; he had a policy of drift.

In contrast to these views, Professor H. Trevor-Roper maintains the

Fig. 7.4. Personality of the leader or national aspirations? Hitler speaking to saluting crowd at Nuremberg. (Photograph by courtesy of Associated Press.)

theory that Hitler took a calculated risk of war in 1939, in that it was physically necessary for him to detach Poland from the West before he could invade Russia from Germany, and that since Hitler's *blitzkrieg* technique was in practice so successful against Poland, western continental Europe and Russia, he must therefore have been well prepared for these operations.

Clearly one requires the full texts of all diplomatic exchanges in the years up to the outbreak of war, and the strengths, both in men and armaments, of the various armies. But even this information is not enough to disprove either one of these theories; one also requires information (as quantitative as possible) on the morale of the armies, and, further, an understanding, from his speeches and writings, of Hitler's basic attitude towards the likelihood of his actions leading to general war in 1939. It is because of the absence of so much of this information that the controversy still remains unresolved.

Taylor and Trevor-Roper are agreed, however, upon one theory, which is that Hitler was a *sounding-board* for German outlook and ambitions, that he achieved what he did because a great many German people shared his ambitions to undo the treaty of Versailles, to destroy Poland, and to invade Russia.

Analysis of historical change *is* important; it corresponds, in Popper's analogy, to letting a searchlight play upon the past, hoping that, by its reflections, it will cast some light on the present. For example, the dual emphasis to be placed on the personality of leaders and on national aspirations is relevant to the present political movements in Cuba, in the Middle East, and in France. At least it gives us a theory on which we may base our present studies and even cautious action, although close observations to determine what new factors are operating must always continue.

General Douglas MacArthur's attitude to the military occupation of Japan after World War II illustrates the efficacy of observation of historical precedents. Describing his approach in 1945 to the task of being supreme commander there, he wrote that "history clearly showed that no modern military occupation of a conquered nation had been a success.... If any occupation lasts too long, or is not carefully watched from the start, one party becomes slaves and the other masters. History teaches, too, that almost every military occupation breeds new wars of the future. I had studied the lives of Alexander and Caesar and Napoleon, and great as these captains were, all had erred when they became the leaders of occupation forces....With such hazards as I anticipated, could I succeed? My doubts were to be my best safeguard, my fears my greatest strength.

"From the moment of my appointment as supreme commander, I had formulated the policies I intended to follow, implementing them through the Emperor and the machinery of the imperial government. I was thoroughly familiar with Japanese administration, its weakness and its strengths, and felt the reforms I contemplated were those which would bring Japan abreast of modern progressive thought and action. First destroy the military power. Punish war criminals. Build the structure of representative government. Modernize the constitution. Hold free elections. Enfranchise the women. Release the political prisoners. Liberate the farmers. Establish a free labour movement. Encourage a free economy. Abolish police oppression. Develop a free and responsible press. Liberalize education. Decentralize the political power. Separate church from state.

"These tasks were to occupy me for the next five years and more. All were eventually accomplished, some easily, some with difficulty. But as the reforms progressed and freedom increasingly came to the Japanese masses, a unique bond of mutual faith developed between the Japanese people and the supreme commander. As they increasingly sensed my insistence upon just treatment for them, even at times against the great nations I represented, they came to regard me not as a conqueror, but as a protector. . . . I have always felt that one of the things that made the occupation a success was my insistence that we wanted to learn from the Japanese as well as teach them. It had a great deal to do with restoring a sense of dignity and purpose in their people, and as they regained self-respect and pride, they approached an exchange of ideas with avidity and good will. This mutual respect became the foundation of the basic esteem our two peoples came to have for one another—and enabled the occupation to write a unique and warmly human chapter of world history."

Many other important examples of historical theories, or points of view, are to be found in historical novels, for example in Tolstoy's "War and Peace" and Sartre's "Les Chemins de la Liberté"; incidentally these books illustrate again the importance of what is called "the will of the nation." They also illustrate the difficulty of expressing, in precise terms, exactly what is meant by "the will" or "the climate of opinion" of a nation. Are the people bored? Do they want peace at almost any price? Do they prefer to spend their money on Bingo or Higher Education? Are they proud of national "adventures" abroad?

Possibly future generations will be in a better position than we are to evaluate these complex aspects of human affairs; perhaps they will make use of popular opinion polls. I believe that one might well begin by formulating some simple law stating, for example, that wars (or concentration camps) become possible in a country where a certain percentage (say 20%) of the population is cruel enough to answer "yes" to the question: "Do you believe in exterminating the X's?" Again, one could well assess people's motives from public opinion polls compiled before events occur, with such questions as: "Do you want Y (a) because it will bring you prosperity, or (b) because it will bring you prestige, or (c) because the Leader says it is good?" Better still, one could ask "Do you want Y?" both before and after the Leader mentions the subject Y, thus getting a measure of the influence of the Leader. The results could then be inserted into eq. (xiv), allowing for coupling between the factors, as for example a "resonance" between the mood of the populace and the ambitions of the leading personalities.

ECONOMIC THEORIES

In economics, simple theories abound. We are all aware of many simple rules about when to buy and sell shares. Economic theories of this type conform to eq. (xv) above, as do theories that the economy always moves in cycles such as boom slump boom or war boom slump. But such theories have proved either too vague to be of real interest or are demonstrably false; new factors are always arising and complicating the picture, as seen in Fig. 7.5. There are thus no inevitable economic laws unless the society under consideration can be completely isolated from outside influences, which is, of course, impossible. Many of the new factors in recent years which have affected economic affairs stem from increasing governmental control. One may cite partial or

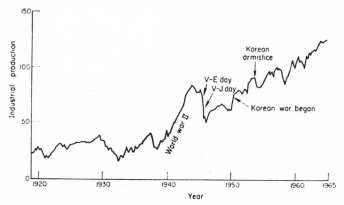

FIG. 7.5. Business ups and downs in the U.S. as measured by industrial production (Federal Reserve Index). The industrial production in the years 1957–59 is arbitrarily taken as 100.

complete controls of the bank rate, of steel prices in the U.S., of government civil spending, of credit, of the rate of supply of money, of sales taxes and purchase taxes, and of income tax. This gives each country a greater measure of control than in former generations over its economy, smoothing the fluctuations in production (cf. Fig. 7.5): social objectives determine economic factors.

An example of a realistic economic theory relates to the growth of a nation's economy and the relation of this growth to rising prices. Rapidly rising prices (or a threat of these) are undesirable in that they cause a "run" on the currency reserves of the nation, i.e. foreign holders of the currency in question sell their holdings.

What factors cause rapidly rising prices? One possibility is high consumer demand; another is an increase in wages in excess of

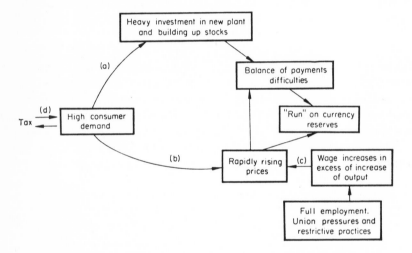

FIG. 7.6. Simplified scheme of inter-related economic factors.

the increase of output. Of course high consumer demand can also be very beneficial, encouraging industry to invest in new plant; at the same time industry will build up its stocks, thus possibly leading again to difficulties in the balance of payments, with the consequent risk of a "run" on the currency reserves. Fig. 7.6 illustrates a rather simplified economic theory; it does not take into account the built-in stabilizers of the system, nor the rate of supply of money.

Now in order to predict from this simplified theory how (for example) most effectively to promote the expansion of the economy without causing too serious a "run" on the currency reserves, we have to know not only the magnitudes concerned, but the "resistances" and "rate-constants" of steps (a), (b), (c) and (d). This particular prediction is very important. For example, if in the situation prevailing, steps (a) and (b) occur readily compared with step (c), action by the government (to prevent prices rising too quickly and hence causing a "run" on the nation's reserves) must necessarily be taken to curb the high consumer demand by imposing additional taxes.

If, on the other hand, step (c) is, at some moment, more important than step (b) in determining how prices rise, i.e., if (c) has a lower resistance than (b), then extra taxes to reduce the consumer demand will merely reduce investment in new plant, needlessly slowing down the expansion of the economy, while prices continue to rise. According to Norman Macrae, the latter situation obtained in Britain in 1955, 1957 and 1961; the action of the Government at these times in curbing demand by taxation was therefore wrong.

Similarly the effect of a financial policy involving central bank action (e.g. of increasing the rate of supply of money into circulation) can be predicted accurately only if the resistances and rate character-istics of steps (d), (a) and (b) are known; lags of 12 to 18 months are reported by Milton Friedman between a change in the rate of supply of money by central bank action and the effect this produces on business conditions in the U.S.A.

The Canadian economy, from the studies of Macesich, apparently also reacts after a time-lag that is both long and variable. And for the U.K., Professor Walters at Birmingham University has come to the provisional conclusion that the time-lag in the effect of govern-mental financial policy is between one and two years.

Economic theories are particularly difficult to study even by the methods of operational research because the system is so susceptible to outside disturbances. In particular, with the improvement of com-munications many new influences can arise, for example, a pronounce-ment on Cuba, Berlin or South-East Asia made by the Russian leader can swiftly and drastically affect the economies of Western countries. And also beyond quantitative measurement at present is the important factor of the climate of opinion, of whether people are in a mood for spending or for saving.

Only by adopting the principle of rigorous testing of theoretical predictions, including those of history and economics, with data which could conceivably disprove them can we possibly distinguish between the different interpretations. Even if some general theory connects a very wide range of historical data, its predictions are never inevitable:

they have no logical status, though they may well be better than uninformed guesses.

Extrapolation into the future of complicated functions is necessarily fraught with great uncertainties, and in human affairs our own consciousness of our ability to change our environment towards different social objectives is a highly significant factor in determining how the future will differ from the past.

Our historical and economic theories, and our testing of them, are important in giving us a better understanding of what variables have been significant in the past. Though admittedly never omniscient, we can thereby attain a somewhat stronger position for controlling the future.

References

Blackett, P. M. S. (1962). "Studies of War", Oliver and Boyd, Edinburgh and London.

Blackstone, B. (1949). "Virginia Woolf", p. 21, Hogarth, London.

Colby, K. M. (1964). Quoted in the *Sunday Times*, London, 12th April.

Constant, H. (1954). *Proc. roy. Inst. Gt. Br.*, **35**, 725.

Darwin, Charles (1931). "Autobiography" (Sir Francis Darwin, ed.), London.

Darwin, Charles (1962). "The Structure and Distribution of Coral Reefs (1842)", reprinted by University of California Press, Berkeley.

Darwin, Charles (1962). *In* "A Century of Darwin" (S. A. Barnett, ed.), Mercury Books, London.

Davies, J. T. (1956). "On Extrapolation", *Brit. J. Phil. Sci.*, **7**, 129.

Davies, J. T. (1964). *In* "The Critical Approach to Science and Philosophy" (M. Bunge, ed.), p. 255, Free Press of Glencoe.

Durrell, L., "The Alexandria Quartet", Faber and Faber, London.

Eddington, A. S. (1933). "The Expanding Universe", Cambridge University Press.

Eddington, A. S. (1939). "The Philosophy of Physical Science", Cambridge University Press.

Eddington, A. S. (1946). "Fundamental Theory", Cambridge University Press.

Edwards, R. S., and Clark, D. (1963). "Planning for Expansion in Electricity Supply"; see especially pages 5, 49, 51.

Einstein, A. (1918). "Motiv des Forschens". *In* "Zu Max Plancks 60. Geburtstag", Ansprachen in der Deutschen Physikalischen Gesellschaft, Karlsruhe, Müller.

Einstein, A. (1921). "Geometrie und Erfahrung", Springer, Berlin; English translation in "Sidelights on Relativity", translated by G. B. Jeffrey and W. Perrett, Methuen, London (1922).

Einstein, A. (1930). "Raum, Äther und Feld in der Physik". *Forum Philosophicum*, **1**, 173.

Einstein, A. (1931). "Maxwell's influence on the development of the conception of physical reality". *In* "James Clerk Maxwell, a Commemoration Volume", p. 66, Cambridge University Press.

Einstein, A. (1934). "Mein Weltbild", translated by Alan Harris, Amsterdam.

Einstein, A. (1934). "The World as I See It", New York; London (1935).

Franklin, Benjamin (1937). *In* "Famous American Men of Science", Crowther, London.

Friedman, M. (1961). *J. Political Economy*, 453.

Friedman, M., and Schwartz, A. J. (1963). *Review of Economics and Statistics*, **45**, 32.

Kekulé, F. A. (1958). *In* "An Introduction to Organic Chemistry", by J. Read, London.

Ladd, H. S., Ingerson, E., Townsend, R. C., Russell, M., Stephenson, H. K. (1953). *Bull. Amer. Ass. Petroleum Geologists*, **37**, 2257.

Lucretius, T. Carus (1951). "The Nature of the Universe" (Latham trans.), Penguin Books, Harmondsworth, England.

MacArthur, D. (1964). "Reminiscences", pp. 282–283, McGraw-Hill, New York.

Macesich, G. (1961). Quoted by Friedman.

Macrae, N. (1963). "Sunshades in October", London.

Markham, S. F. (1947). "Climate and the Energy of Nations", Oxford.

Miller, A. J. (1963). *Operations Research*, **11**, 236.

Mumford, L. S. (1963). *Chem. & Ind.*, 1788.

Popper, Sir Karl R. (1933). *Erkenntnis*, **3**, 426.

Popper, Sir Karl R. (1959). "The Logic of Scientific Discovery", Hutchinson, London; first published Vienna (1935).

Popper, Sir Karl R. (1945). "The Open Society and its Enemies", Vol. 2, 1st Ed. (4th Ed. 1962), George Routledge & Sons Ltd., London. For scientific method see especially pp. (4th Ed.) 213–214, 259–266 and Chapter 25, note 3. For discussion on Marxism, see particularly Chapter 15, notes 14 and 16; Chapter 18, note 17; Chapter 19 (ii), and Chapter 20 (vi).

Popper, Sir Karl R. (1963). "Conjectures and Refutations", Routledge and Kegan Paul, London. See especially pp. 34, 36, 46, 47.

Pritchett, V. R. (1956). "All about Ourselves". *In New Statesmen*, 26th May. Quoted by R. Pascal in "Design and Truth in Autobiography", Routledge and Kegan Paul, London, 1960.

Rayleigh, Lord (1899). *Phil. Mag.* **48**, 321.

Report from the Select Committee on Nationalized Industries (1963). "The Electricity Supply Industry", Vol. 1, H.M.S.O., London. See especially pp. 31, 32, 34, 35, 37.

Russell, B. (1947). "History of Western Philosophy", George Allen and Unwin Ltd., London. See especially p. 235.

Snow, Lord (C. P. Snow) (1964). "The Two Cultures and a Second Look", Cambridge University Press.

Spengler, O. (1934). "The Decline of the West" (C. F. Atkinson trans.), George Allen and Unwin Ltd.

Taton, R. (ed.) (1963, 1964). "A General History of the Sciences", Vols. 1 and 2, Thames and Hudson, London.

Taylor, A. J. P. (1961). "The Origins of the Second World War", London.

Trevor-Roper, H. R. (1961). *Encounter* (London), **17**, 88.

Waddington, C. H. (1962). "Theories of Evolution". *In* "A Century of Darwin", Mercury Books, London.

Walters, A. A. (1964). Private communication, 13th March.

Watt, James (1859). *In* "Reminiscences of James Watt", by R. Hart, *Trans. Glasgow Archaeological Soc.*

Yonge, C. M. (1962). "Darwin and the Coral Reefs". *In* "A Century of Darwin", Mercury Books, London.

Zeuner, F. E. (1961). Address to Convocation, University of London, 9th May. See also Gibbon E. (1963), "The Decline and Fall of the Roman Empire" (abridged by D. M. Low), 474–475. Chatto and Windus, London.

Index

Analogies in science, 12, 59
Ancient world, 18, 22–27, 82–83
Astrology, 37
Atoms, 14–16, 24–26, 60–66
Attributes of a scientific theory, 40

Bacon, F., 19
Benzene ring, 14–16, 56
Bion, 27
Bucket analogy of mind, 3

Civilization and science, 82 ff
Coin tossing, 6
Confidence, 40–42, 45, 50–52, 68, 72
Convention in science, 54, 58–59
Copernicus, 18–19
Coral islands, 12, 23
Credibility, 6, 40–41, 50

Darwin, Charles, 12–14, 23–24, 53
Democritus, 24

Economic theories, 93 ff
Eddington, Sir A. S., 20–21, 29, 37, 39
Education, 1, 84
Einstein, Albert, 1, 28, 41, 54
Epicurus, 24
Eratosthenes, 27
Excellence of a theory, 11, 41–42, 48, 50

Falsifiability of scientific theories, 31, 32 ff
Forecasting market trends, 73 ff
Franklin, Benjamin, 26

Galileo, 8, 19, 22, 39

Historical theories, 89 ff
Historical writings, 3, 92
Hypothesis, 12, 41

Kekulé, 14–16, 56

Law, definition of, 5, 41
Law, simple, 40
Logic, 4, 5, 17
Lucretius, 24

MacArthur, General Douglas, 91–92
Mathematics, 5, 7, 10, 17
Mind, theories of, 2–4
Molecules, 14–16, 24–25, 49, 58–66

Naphthalene, 14–16
Newton and his theories, 8–9, 20, 22–23, 36, 39, 41, 57, 69

Objectivity, 1–4, 11
Operational research, 86 ff
Origin of theories, 1, 11 ff

Plane-tracking analogy, 33–37, 39, 51
Pliny, 26
Popper, Professor Sir Karl, 1–3, 28, 31, 33, 37, 43, 89, 91
Predictions, 17, 32 ff, 40, 68 ff
Probability theory, 6–7, 17, 80
Psychoanalytical theories, 37
Pythagoras, 18, 26

Rare gases, 38
Reality of particles, 61–65

Reformation, 18–19, 31
Refutation of theories, 18–19, **29–35**, 38–41
Renaissance, 18, 31
Russell, Bertrand, 6, 26

Scientific theory, 32–33, 40
Searchlight analogy of the mind making predictions from general theories, 2, 32 ff, 91
Simplicity, 54 ff
Snow, Lord, v, 85

Specialization in education, 1, 84
Subjectivity, 1–4, 11
Symmetry, 65, 67

Taylor, A. J. P., 90–91
Trevor-Roper, H., 90–91
Truth of general theories, 4, 5, 7, 20
Two cultures, v, 84, 85

Watt, James, 43
Weather forecasts, 37, 72
Western civilization, 82